SERTUM ANGLICUM

FACSIMILE

WITH CRITICAL STUDIES

AND A TRANSLATION

Lycoris aurea (Amaryllis aurea)
From original drawing by Redouté, reproduced in *Sertum Anglicum* in Pl. 15 *bis*

Charles-Louis L'Héritier de Brutelle

SERTUM ANGLICUM

1788

FACSIMILE
WITH CRITICAL STUDIES
AND A TRANSLATION

THE HUNT BOTANICAL LIBRARY
PITTSBURGH, PENNSYLVANIA

1963

Number 1 of The Hunt Facsimile Series
Editor: George H. M. Lawrence
Director, The Hunt Botanical Library

Printed in Holland
1963

Foreword

In recent years there has been a marked increase in the production of facsimile editions of works proven by time to be unusually valuable or useful. Technological refinements in photo-offset reproduction methods have made it possible to produce facsimiles of high quality at reasonable prices, even at a time when printing costs spiral upwards. In the field of natural history, and especially that of the plant sciences, the past decade has witnessed a burgeoning of facsimile works, among which the Ray Society's production of Linnaeus's *Species plantarum*—because of its scholarly introductory treatises by W. T. Stearn and J. L. Heller—stands apart from all others in exemplifying a new concept of the service that a facsimile production can render. The establishment of The Hunt Facsimile Series, of which this work is the first number, was motivated in large part by the conviction of its editor that the Ray Society concept of new studies accompanying the original work is a contribution vital to the renewed availability and expanded usefulness of the original.

The Hunt Facsimile Series will be composed of titles of current importance to the working taxonomist, of historical interest to the economic botanist and horticulturist, or of aesthetic value to the connoisseur of botanical illustration. The major effort in the production of each title lies in the research studies for the several introductory accounts that must accompany the reproduction of the original text and illustrations. The extent of prerequisite research often will determine the frequency of appearance of volumes in this series. The selection of titles to be produced rests largely with the Advisory Committee of the Hunt Botanical Library. Within the subject area noted above the Committee has selected titles that commercial interests are unlikely to reproduce.

A primary editorial policy for all volumes of this series is to ensure that the introductions accompanying the facsimile proper provide information hitherto unavailable in standard works of reference. An approach to this objective is illustrated by the introductory essays of this first volume.

L'Héritier de Brutelle's *Sertum Anglicum* was chosen for the first production in this series because it met several requirements: it is rare, since fewer than one hundred copies are believed to have been published, of which fewer than fifty have been located; it is taxonomically of considerable importance, since in it were described thirteen new genera and sixty-five new species (from a total of thirty-five genera and 124 species for the entire work); it is illustrated by two famous botanical artists of the 18th and 19th centuries, Pierre-Joseph Redouté and James Sowerby; it is of interest to horticulturists, since its subject matter is very largely of plants that were then newly introduced to gardens of the London and Paris areas; and, although the original is a broadsheet production (one in which the sheets are printed and bound without folding, in contrast to a folio work in which they are folded once), and is of large dimension, it is of comparatively few pages and thus producible at moderate cost.

The facsimile reproduction of the thirty-five plates is from a copy of *Sertum Anglicum* at The Houghton Library, Harvard College, made available through the courtesy of Professor William A. Jackson, Librarian. The reproduction of the original text is from the copy at the Rachel McMasters Miller Hunt Botanical Library, Carnegie Institute of Technology.

The full life story of L'Héritier may never be unravelled, and the story behind the production of this work continues to leave some aspects unresolved, but the account by Dr. Stafleu that follows is as fascinating as a modern cloak and dagger mystery. No other botanist has the dubious distinction, which is L'Héritier's, of being sabred to death, at night, near his home in the outskirts of Paris. To determine the framework of this story and to fill in the details (of which there are far more than available space could accommodate), Dr. Stafleu consulted scores of letters by L'Héritier and his correspondents, now preserved at the British Museum (largely in the Banks Collection), a great many other letters at the Linnean Society of London (in the J. E. Smith archives), and other notes and manuscripts at the British Museum (Natural History) in London. In various Paris institutions, as well as in Geneva, he found more original documents and associated correspondence. Because of the dispersal of this material the services of Professor Jacques Rousseau were called on to assist him in ferreting out information in the multitude of archival reservoirs in Paris and Geneva and to arrange for the microfilm to be made of it. Professor Rousseau's investigations took him therefore to the De Candolle collections at Geneva, where he also consulted a substantial quantity of L'Héritier's manuscripts and additional correspondence acquired by Augustin P. De Candolle after L'Héritier's death. Microfilm records of this raw material were made and are on file at the Hunt Botanical Library. Two sets of xerox prints were made from the microfilms—one for Dr. Stafleu in Utrecht, and one for the Hunt Botanical Library.

The thirty-five plates in *Sertum Anglicum* are botanically important because thirty-one of them are the first published illustrations, and seven are the only known illustrations, of the species concerned. For reasons which Wilfrid Blunt explains in his study of them, they do not exemplify the better work of Redouté or of Sowerby. Blunt's study of the engraved productions owes much of its value to the availability for comparison of two of Redouté's original wash drawings from which plates were later engraved for the *Sertum Anglicum*. These are from the Hunt Botanical Library's substantial collection of Redouté originals acquired by Mrs. Hunt over the years. Both originals are reproduced in this facsimile for the first time, one (the frontispiece) in color. Their acquisition in 1954, through a dealer who purchased them that year in Paris (but no others from the *Sertum*), suggests that the other originals also are now widely dispersed. These two are the only Redouté originals for the *Sertum* that have been located, and the Hunt Botanical Library invites reports of known locations of any others. No originals by Sowerby have been located. It has been known since the publication of the *Sertum* that plates 13 and 17 are by Bruguière, a man better known as a traveller and plant collector than as a botanical artist (*cf.* p. *lvii*). When Wilfrid Blunt and Dr. Stafleu searched for records, Miss Phyllis I. Edwards, departmental librarian, found in the herbarium at the British Museum (Natural History) among the specimens of *Carpolyza tenella,* a small wash drawing of the plant by Bruguière on which he had written that he had sketched it while collecting it at the Cape of Good Hope. This small original also is reproduced in Mr. Blunt's introduction.

Facsimiles of taxonomic works published before the present century require updating to be of maximum current use. The text of the *Sertum* is both horticultural and taxonomic, and a useful evaluation of both facets is presented by Messrs Gilmour, King, and Williams. This evaluation has entailed a search for the herbarium specimens cited and studied by L'Héritier. For a majority of the included species, notations concerning his type specimens are given when the types were located. A valuable contribution is the list of L'Héritier's plants, giving their generally accepted modern names; these will enable present-day readers to link up L'Héritier's species with information on the same plants in modern botanical and horticultural works of reference. The historical notes on the recorded date of introduction of each species add to the very fragmentary data provided by L'Héritier.

Today working botanical taxonomists read Latin descriptions of plants with facility. L'Héritier presented his entire work in Latin, and the recognition that his narrative passages, accounting for many interesting details, could not be read as easily as the descriptions, prompted the inclusion of an English translation of all parts except the Latin names and their literature citations, and the simple Latin descriptions of genera and species. L'Héritier's Latin is well written, but it is neither the classical Latin of Cicero nor the vulgar Latin of the Renaissance. To translate it one must be a botanist as well as a Latinist. These considerations led me to the nearby Saint Vincent Archabbey (at Latrobe, Pennsylvania), a Benedictine monastery and college whose magnificent library is considered the second largest collection of early religious works in America, whose President is a taxonomic botanist, whose Prior took his degree in classical languages at Cornell University and heads the Latin Department at Saint Vincent, and whose Professor of Medieval Musicology has studied extensively in both Paris and Italy, working almost exclusively with Latin works and manuscripts. This trio of interested monks volunteered their services and pooled their knowledge to provide the translation that precedes the facsimile proper. In the course of their deliberations the two who are non-scientists learned some botany, while the eavesdropping editor absorbed more Latin.

The principal authors of the three introductory essays were selected because of earlier studies made in these and allied fields. Dr. Frans A. Stafleu, of the Botanical Museum, University of Utrecht, and of the International Association for Plant Taxonomy, is widely known among taxonomists as a specialist on the botanical literature and authors of the later part of the 18th century. Mr. Wilfrid Blunt, Curator of the Watts Gallery, near Guildford, England, and author of *The Art of Botanical Illustration*

(1950), is an internationally recognized critic on botanical artists and their work. Mr. John S. L. Gilmour, Director of the University Botanic Garden, Cambridge, England, is a leading authority on cultivated plants in Britain and on the extensive literature about them. He was assisted by Mr. C. J. King, Librarian, The University Botanic Garden, Cambridge, and Mr. L. H. J. Williams, Senior experimental officer, Department of Botany, British Museum (Natural History), London.

Acknowledgement is given here to many persons other than the principals for their contributions to the research studies and the production of this volume. Professor Jacques Rousseau, formerly of the Montreal Botanic Garden, later of the Sorbonne, and now at Lavalle University, Quebec, with unbounded interest and enthusiasm sought out an abundance of unpublished material on the life of L'Héritier and the production of his *Sertum,* finding it in many of the repositories known to him through his own bibliographic studies of eighteenth century French botanists. Mr. James Dandy, Keeper of the Department of Botany, British Museum (Natural History), was most generous in making available all of the records in his charge. Miss Phyllis I. Edwards, Librarian, and Dr. W. T. Stearn, Senior scientific officer, at the herbarium of the Department of Botany at the British Museum (Natural History) provided many bibliographic and taxonomic details, including elucidation of L'Héritier's rather enigmatic use of the abbreviation *Licet. spont.* (see p. *xcv* for explanation). Especial thanks are expressed to the Trustees of the British Museum (Natural History) for permission to reproduce Bruguière's original drawing of *Carpolyza tenella,* and to the London Sunday Times for permission to reproduce, from its issue of 14 February 1937, Hanslip Fletcher's drawing of Sir Joseph Banks's residence at Soho Square, made shortly before the building was razed. Thanks are given to the directors and librarians who provided bibliographic reports on copies of *Sertum Anglicum* in their charge, incorporated here in the table on p. *xl.* Likewise, thanks are extended to the curators responsible for documentary records consulted in the course of these investigations, and especially to those in charge of the records that were microfilmed at the Académie des Sciences, Paris; Bibliothèque de l'Institut, Paris; the Bibliothèque Nationale, Paris; The British Museum; The British Museum (Natural History); the Linnean Society of London; the Muséum National d'Histoire naturelle, Phanérogamie, Paris; the Conservatoire de Botanique, Geneva, and the Biohistorical Institute of the University of Utrecht. Of paramount importance are our thanks to Dr. William A. Jackson for his generous loan of Harvard College's Houghton Library copy of *Sertum Anglicum* from which were reproduced the plates of this volume. Thanks are extended also to the Hunt Botanical Library staff, which has been most helpful in the production of this volume; notably Mr. Ian MacPhail for his bibliographic studies, and Mr. Willem Margadant for his reading of manuscripts and proofs, and assistance in preparing the indices. The production of the entire work was entrusted to Joh. Enschedé en Zonen, Haarlem, Holland, and to all members of the firm who took such personal interest and who made such a painstaking effort in the manufacture of this volume, we are pleased to extend our thanks.

G. H. M. LAWRENCE, Editor

Contents

L'Héritier de Brutelle: the man and his work

F. A. Stafleu

THE MAN

Charles-Louis L'Héritier de Brutelle, the aristocrat who had so eagerly adopted the principles of the French revolution, the straight-forward and honest magistrate of both the old and the new régimes, the fervent Linnaean botanist, who as an amateur and self-made scientist had found his way to the highest ranks of the French Academy of Sciences, was assassinated in the late evening of 28 thermidor of the eighth year of the French revolution (16 August 1800). The murder took place at a very short distance from his house, where his children were awaiting him, but it was only at dawn that his body was found, brutally hewn down by sabre cuts. The murder has remained a mystery ever since, a mystery illustrative of the whole life of this incomprehensible man, full of contradictions and unexpected achievements, a man who was awe-inspiring as a magistrate, impressive in his fanatical approach to botany, but whose great tragedy in life was the failure to understand and educate his eldest son. It was perhaps this failure that was the direct cause of his brutal death.

Even now, more than 160 years after his death, it is extremely difficult to judge the man L'Héritier. He consistently refused to have his portrait made. In his extensive correspondence there are rarely remarks of a personal nature. Even in his public quarrels, L'Héritier showed great restraint and reserve and seldom betrayed human emotion. As a judge he was well known for this attitude of a strict and almost impersonal correctitude. As a botanist he was an ardent Linnaean disciple, more Linnaean than Linnaeus, not at all philosophically inclined, but greatly attracted by the ever further unfolding variety of nature and primarily concerned with classification rather than understanding.

EARLY LIFE

Charles-Louis L'Héritier de Brutelle was born in Paris on 15 June 1746. We know little or nothing of his parents, except that they were rather wealthy Roman Catholics, and that they belonged to the court circles. They must have had sufficient influence to obtain for him in 1772 the fairly high administrative position of superintendent of the waters and forests of the Paris region (*Procureur du roi à la maîtrise des eaux et des forêts de la généralité de Paris*). Although this position was predominantly administrative, and eminently suited to be enjoyed as a sinecure, L'Héritier undertook it in a characteristic way. He had been appointed with little or no knowledge at all of forestry and now that he had been assigned to this job his interest was awakened.

Cuvier, in his biography (1802), relates how L'Héritier together with a group of his colleagues, visited the Paris Botanic Garden, amusing themselves by naming the trees, that they encountered. The fourth tree, a *Celtis,* growing in the open air in the garden, was unknown to them. L'Héritier could not bear this defeat before his friends and it stimulated him to go further into botany. He had already made himself acquainted with the vegetative characteristics of the native French shrubs and trees, but from then on he devoted himself also to the study of exotic plants, especially those that could be introduced more generally into cultivation in France. His botanical training was that of a self-made man: we know of no courses taken by him, no one of his contemporaries can be said to have been his teacher. L'Héritier himself evidently regarded Linnaeus as his great master and he remained faithful to him until the end. Cuvier explains this predilection for Linnaeus, which was not shared by his fellow botanists at the botanical institutions of Paris, by distinguishing three types of plant taxonomists: the aesthetics, the classifiers, and the philosophers. L'Héritier obviously belonged to the second category; the first category cannot now be called plant taxonomists in any modern sense, and the third category was represented in France by such men as Michel Adanson [1727-1806] and Antoine-Laurent de Jussieu [1748-1826]. L'Héritier was not so much concerned with the discovery of the natural relationships between the plants as with their classification and identification. This approach to botany was in keeping with his character, but it did not help to bring him closer to the genial and clever leader of the professional botanists, A. L. de Jussieu. It must be said at once, however, that in later life, after the revolution, L'Héritier showed a greater appreciation for the natural system, as well as for its proponents Adanson and A. L. de Jussieu, than in his productive years.

THE "COUR DES AIDES"

In 1775 L'Héritier was appointed counsellor at the *Cour des Aides* at Paris. This appointment meant that he became a judge and that he was becoming a man of law rather than an economic administrator. The *Cour des Aides* was one of the Paris law-courts of the old regime, dealing with all affairs that concerned the state revenue obtained by indirect taxes (*aides*). From the point of view of "society" it was not the most important law-court, but through it L'Héritier came into contact with all layers of the Paris community of his days, and in addition it gave him a sufficiently high status as a magistrate. This appointment also brought him in closer contact with one of France's most eminent men, de Malesherbes, a contact from which arose a warm friendship. More important, however, is the circumstance that through Malesherbes L'Héritier became a member of a body that played a primary rôle in the development of the socially advanced ideas of the Enlightenment, and that formed the only organised group of magistrates that stood openly for the protection of the interests of the "underprivileged."

The history of the *Cour des Aides* would merit a chapter by itself, and has indeed been told in full in several places. The part of this history relevant here is connected mainly with that of its president, Malesherbes, and with its influence on L'Héritier's development as an enlightened magistrate and aristocrat who successfully survived the difficult years of the French revolution.

The first two lines of the title-page of the *Sertum Anglicum* are: "Car. Lud. L'Héritier, Dom. de Brutelle, *in Aulâ Juvam. Par. Reg. Consil.*" (*in Aulâ Juvǎminum Parisiensi, Regis Consiliarius*). The italicized words give L'Héritier's status as counsellor at this fiscal court. Similar indications are found on most of his other publications. One might well ask why the legal title was so consistently introduced, when it had nothing to do with botany or any other science. Evidently L'Héritier attributed great importance to this post and when we look at the position of the *Cour des Aides* in late eighteenth century France we can understand this: it labelled L'Héritier as belonging to that small, socially progressive group of influential magistrates that did so much to prepare the way for the revolution that was to come.

The Paris *Cour des Aides,* one of France's oldest law courts (it dates from the end of the 14th century) acted, in fact, as the supreme fiscal court of France. While it dealt with all kinds of petty crimes committed by taxpayers, it also protected them, and in general the small landowners, farmers, and tradesmen against abuse of authority in financial matters by a corrupt and thoroughly decadent administration.

The man who had such a great influence on the development of L'Héritier, Chrétien-Guillaume de Lamoignon-Malesherbes, born on 6 December 1721 (and hence nearly twenty-five years older than L'Héritier), was appointed counsellor at this court on 26 February 1749, and, more important, First President on 14 December 1750. In this capacity, which he combined with that of head of the censorship of the press and the book trade, Malesherbes could develop his great gifts as a magistrate. The famous *Encyclopédie* of Diderot and D'Alembert was published in this period and admitted by Malesherbes. What this meant for the development and diffusion of scientifically and socially advanced ideas need not be stressed here. The *Cour des Aides,* in those years, waged a veritable war against state ministers and other high government officials who used their powers unscrupulously in the collection of taxes. This struggle culminated in 1775, the year L'Héritier was appointed to the court, in the publication of one of the most courageous and enlightening documents published under the old regime and aiming at its reformation. Malesherbes presented a scheme for a far-reaching fiscal reform, providing adequate safeguards against abuse, a scheme accompanied by explanatory notes that implied extensive political and social reforms.

The opposition to this document was such that Malesherbes retired soon after its publication, but not before L'Héritier and he had laid the foundation for a life-long friendship. L'Héritier, whose strong sense of duty and justice is known to us from his courageous conduct during the days of the revolution, must have felt greatly honored and pleased to become a member of a body which, during the last twenty-five years, had become a symbol of justice in the midst of universal injustice and corruption.

Malesherbes was typically an encyclopedist. His interests and knowledge were wide: by profession a lawyer, he was a good historian, and greatly interested in the literature and arts of his days. He had also a great predilection for the natural sciences, especially botany, an interest that had already been recognized, as early as 1750, by his election as a honorary member of the Academy of Sciences. In 1776 after a short term as minister of state charged with the affairs of the police, Malesherbes retired to a quiet country-life, only to return to political life for a short time in 1787. Malesherbes' tragic fate is well known: he was one of the counsel of Louis XVI when the king was put on trial before the National Convention. In December 1793 Malesherbes was arrested and accused of conspiracy against the unity of the republic. After having refused to defend himself against what was to him a ridiculous charge, he was guillotined on 22 April 1794.

Malesherbes probably had more influence on L'Héritier than any other man, certainly in his opinion of the duties of a magistrate, but very possibly as a man of encyclopedic knowledge, who, besides his professional and many other interests, was, just like L'Héritier himself, an ardent and able amateur botanist. To his *cercle* belonged such men as Jean-Jacques Rousseau [1712-1778] and Thomas Jefferson [1743-1826].

The year 1775 was important for L'Héritier also in another respect. In that year he married Thérèse-Valère Doré; the union lasted for nineteen years. She died in 1794, having born him five children. As with the other private affairs of L'Héritier, we know very little of his married life. His friend Cuvier (1802) assures us that it was a happy life, but none of his other friends, *e.g.*, Desherbiers (1801) and J. E. Smith (1811), add anything material to this statement. After his wife's death, L'Héritier remained single, and devoted himself to the education of his children and to his professional duties.

CONTACT WITH SIR JOSEPH BANKS

The botanical activities of L'Héritier first became public with the appearance of the first fascicle of his *Stirpes novae* in March 1785. Before that time he was already in contact with colleagues abroad, notably Sir Joseph Banks [1748-1820]. Since his acquaintance with this eminent British aristocrat led directly to the production of the *Sertum Anglicum*, it is of great importance that, thanks to Banks' careful saving of documents, the letters by and on L'Héritier have been carefully preserved at the British Museum. They enable us to follow in detail the momentous events in L'Héritier's life that ultimately resulted in the *Sertum Anglicum* as a token of gratitude to English botany and botanists. Part of this correspondence was used previously by James Britten [1826-1924] and Bernard Barham Woodward [1853-1930] in their thirty-fifth "Bibliographical Note" (1905) which dealt with L'Héritier's botanical works.

L'Héritier was introduced to Banks by a close friend, Pierre-Marie-Auguste Broussonet [1761-1807], in a letter dated 20 January 1783. Broussonet was a professional botanist trained at Paris. In this letter Broussonet speaks of L'Héritier's exclusive interest in trees and shrubs, as they occur in his own garden, and that he intends to bring out a kind of "dendrology." "[Il] ne fait rien avec les herbacées" (he does nothing with the herbs). On 2 February 1783 L'Héritier writes to Banks, referring to Broussonet, introducing himself and his project of publishing a work on new or imperfectly known woody plants: "à raison de la predilection avec laquelle je les ai toujours etudié et cultivé [*sic*], et comme etant la partie la plus negligée de tous les Botanistes" (because of the predilection with which I have always studied and grown them, and because they are the part

Residence of Sir Joseph Banks, Soho Square, London
After drawing by Hanslip Fletcher, courtesy London *Sunday Times*

that is most neglected by all botanists). [The quotations are here given literally and the omission of diacritic signs, the presence of grammatical errors, etc. correspond with those in the original text.]

The reason why L'Héritier wanted to be in contact with Banks was obvious. The latter's botanical collections and library were famous, and his house at Soho Square may be regarded as the true headquarters of science in London at that time. The collections and books were always available to visiting botanists; and Banks himself, through Daniel Carl Solander [1736-1782] and later through Jonas Dryander [1784-1819] the curators of his collection, and through the stimulus he gave to expeditions for the collection of living and dried plants from all over the world, played a very important rôle in the development of late eighteenth century botany. It was therefore natural that L'Héritier sought Banks' acquaintance, for the latter could give him invaluable information from his collections and library. Furthermore Banks, like L'Héritier, was a fervent follower of Linnaeus, and even at this early date relations between L'Héritier and the Paris botanical establishment were becoming rather cool. L'Héritier was after all an amateur, and was not by nature inclined to the more philosophical approach to the plant kingdom of men like Antoine-Laurent de Jussieu and Adanson, who were pursuing a natural system. L'Héritier wanted to describe and classify new plants: "pu-

[*xvii*]

blier les plantes nouvelles, non figurées ou mal connues, voila quel est mon but" (to publish new plants, not illustrated or badly known, that is my object): nothing less, nothing more.

For this L'Héritier found a sympathetic ear in England, where the Linnaean approach was far more popular than with the more philosophically inclined French botanists. He adds, still in this same first letter to Banks: "Je garde encore le secret sur mon project pour que cette espece de travail ne puisse pas être revendiqué par nos Professeurs qui auroient du l'entreprendre même avant que j'aie eu la premiere notion de plante[s]…" (I am still keeping my project secret, in order that this type of work cannot be claimed by our Professors, who should have undertaken it even before I had the first notion of plants). This phrase quite well illustrates the rather strained relations between L'Héritier the amateur and the *professeurs,* meaning of course the botanical professors at the *Jardin du Roi,* the central Paris natural history institution, now called the *Muséum National d'Histoire naturelle.*

THE FIRST PUBLICATION

The first installment of this book, the *Stirpes novae,* published at his own expense, appeared in March 1785 (bearing the date 1784), and was followed by a second part in January 1786, and a third in March of the same year. The preface is dated 3 December 1783. The book was magnificently produced: "Ses ouvrages étoient superbes; mais sa table étoit frugale et ses habits simples. Il dépensoit vingt mille francs par an pour la botanique, et il alloit a pied" (Cuvier 1802). (His works were superb, but his table frugal and his clothes simple. He spent twenty thousand francs a year on botany, but he went on foot).

The first fascicle shows that L'Héritier had given up his original idea of describing only woody plants. There are several herbs among the first ten species. The first species is *Monetia barlerioides,* belonging to a new genus named after Lamarck [J. B. A. P. Monnet de Lamarck 1744-1829]; he includes a few complimentary lines on the vast work that Lamarck was then undertaking: the compilation of the botanical volumes for the *Encyclopédie methodique;* the first installment had been published on 2 December 1783.

The relations between Lamarck and L'Héritier were not always so cordial as might be supposed from this friendly dedication. In later correspondence Lamarck is often mentioned as irritated by not having been properly cited, or by other improprieties. Lamarck was another difficult man in an era in which France certainly did not lack difficult botanists: Adanson, Lamarck, L'Héritier were all three out of step with the professional botanists at the *Jardin du Roi,* for entirely different reasons. Though this period was very productive for French taxonomy, one can only be disturbed by the mutual envy and jealousy of botanists, and the way in which each tried to hide his findings from the others until he had published them. The atmosphere is strikingly illustrated by an anonymous correspondent of Paulus Usteri [1768-1831], who, in a letter from Paris dated 18 January 1791, writes:

"Langsam gehen dergleichen Arbeiten [as those of L'Héritier] in Paris immer, denn die Botanicker und Liebhaber [*sic*] sind allhier nichts weniger als mittheilend; hat jemand eine seltene Pflanze in der Blüthe so wird sie strenger als irgend ein Schatz bewahrt, wenn die Gärtner für Geld nicht zu Zeiten eine Ausnahme von der Regel machten so würde der Gewinn den die Wissenschaft dabei macht sehr gering seyn" (*Ann. Bot. Usteri* 1: 170. 1792). (This type of work always goes slowly in Paris; the botanists and amateurs here are anything but communicative; when someone has a rare plant in flower, it is guarded more closely than a treasure. If the gardeners did not make an exception from time to time, for money, the gain made by science would be very small.)

Most botanists in those times attached a very high value to undescribed plants, and it sometimes seems as if each considered his eminence as a botanist to be in direct proportion with the number of new species described. L'Héritier, because of his position at Paris, was not able to travel widely and collect new plants himself.

L'Héritier had made it his object to describe the new plants from living specimens, and in order to find the necessary novelties in a city where they were so closely guarded he had to make use of the information that reached him through gardeners or other friends and acquaintances. Léger's story (1945) that L'Héritier had a paid team of young men who kept him informed of the flowering of new plants quite probably has a sound basis. In his preface to the *Stirpes novae* L'Héritier makes a plea to future travellers to entrust him with the publication of their discoveries. This would be [he says] a deposit to be held in trust; the glory and the treasure would be safe, and forgetting his own researches, he would be happy and honored to be the simple editor of those of the travellers. Apart from this it is doubtful whether he was a natural explorer. We know nothing definite even of short trips made in France. He divided his time between his Paris residence and his country seat in Picardy. We can safely assume that he was much more interested in growing plants in his gardens for possible publication than in going out in the field to collect.

The *Stirpes novae* was to become L'Héritier's major work. It was never finished: like the *Sertum Anglicum,* it was doomed to get stuck in the French revolution. Six parts of the former were published, together with a *Conspectus* (pp. 183, 184) giving the contents of a seventh installment that was never published. The book consists of eighty-four plates with accompanying descriptive text. For further details on this publication see Britten and Woodward (1905), Stevenson (1961), and Rickett and Stafleu (1961).

In the second fascicle of the *Stirpes novae* we find the first plates to have been drawn by Pierre-Joseph Redouté [1759-1840]. L'Héritier had "discovered" this artist around 1784. Both men were frequent visitors at the Jardin du Roi, and it can be assumed that it was here that they met. L'Héritier trained Redouté as a botanical artist and gave him access to his private library. The two men became intimate friends. Redouté gracefully remembered L'Héritier much later, in 1817, when, in his *Roses* (vol. 3, p. 22) he said that it had been L'Héritier who had led him to a new career and who had made it possible for him to develop his talents. L'Héritier's feelings for Redouté were not less devoted, as is shown by a manuscript which has remained unpublished and which is now preserved at the Muséum National d'Histoire naturelle. This manuscript is a memoir on a new genus of plants to be called *Redoutea* and in his dedication L'Héritier speaks of Redouté as his true companion in his botanical excursions [*sic*] "... en un mot l'associé insepa-rable de la tâche que j'ai à remplir. Cher Redouté, la verité de ton pinceau bien plus que sa Magie, me fera partager la celebrité que meriteront peut être un jour nos com-muns ouvrages. ..." ("... in a word the associate who is inseparable from the task that I have to fulfil. Dear Redouté, the truth of your brush even more than its magic will let me share with you the celebrity which our common works will perhaps earn some day. ...")

At the time L'Héritier issued his first parts of the *Stirpes novae* he had approached sever-al other botanists with the main purpose of obtaining unknown material. Casimiro Gomez Ortega [1740-1818], professor of botany at Madrid, sent him some plants from Chile, but his greatest hopes were in Joseph Dombey [1742-1793] the French traveller and botanist, who was at that time in Chile and Peru. The main facts of the relations be-tween Dombey and L'Héritier were told for the first time by Sir James Edward Smith [1759-1828] in Rees' *Cyclopedia* (1809, 1811), and have since been quite well known, also thanks to the publication by Britten and Woodward (1905). The story is of eminent importance for the history of the *Sertum Anglicum* and is given here in some detail, based upon the correspondence of L'Héritier, Dryander, Smith, and Banks, preserved in London at the British Museum, the British Museum (Natural History), and the Linnean Society, as well as upon various secondary sources.

THE DOMBEY AFFAIR

Joseph Dombey was a French traveller and botanist whose courageous and tragic life has been the subject of several interesting and excellent treatises (Deleuze 1804; Smith 1809; Lacaze 1855; Hamy 1905). Dombey's South American collections provided the actual incentive for L'Héritier's journey to England in 1786 and for this reason some relevant facts may be briefly recalled here.

Dombey, trained as a doctor of medicine at Montpellier, had changed to botany early in life, mainly under the influence of Philibert Commerson [1727-1773]. He studied botany under Antoine Gouan [1733-1821] at Montpellier and at Paris under Louis-Guil-laume Lemonnier [1717-1799] and the aged Bernard de Jussieu [1699-1777]. Among his good friends were (later) Pierre-Marie-Auguste Broussonet [1761-1807] and André Thouin [1747-1823], who both later became friends of L'Héritier also, as well as Jean-Jacques Rousseau. In 1775 Anne-Robert-Jacques Turgot [1727-1781], the eminent French states-man and convinced physiocrat, at the recommendation of Bernard de Jussieu [1699-1777], appointed Dombey "médecin-botaniste" at the *Jardin du Roi,* with the special task to explore Spanish America in order to find useful plants for possible introduction into France. After negotiations with the Spanish government it was decided that Dombey was to accompany Hipólito Ruiz Lopez [1754-1815] and José Antonio Pavón [1754-1844], both pupils of Gomez Ortega, on their expedition to Peru and Chile organized by that government. Dombey, accepted as a member of this expedition, was to receive his salary from the French government, but had otherwise to give the less experienced

Ruiz and Pavón the benefit of his knowledge of travel and of collecting and forwarding living and dried plants. From the beginning the Spanish government made it clear that of each plant collected by Dombey one specimen should be offered to Spain, except for the unicates, which might be retained by Dombey but of which he had to submit a description or a picture. Dombey was to deposit copies of all his notes and descriptions with the Spanish government. Little doubt remains since the publication of the original records concerning these matters by Agustin Jesús Barreiro (1940), that Dombey was fully acquainted with these conditions, and we also know that he painstakingly observed the agreement. On the other hand the records disclose that the Spanish government definitely aimed at profiting as much as possible from Dombey's knowledge and skill even when his salary was fully paid by the French, without leaving him much chance ever to extract much profit out of this venture for the benefit of his own country. The story of all his adventures in Peru and Chile, from his arrival at Callao in 1778 until his departure in 1784 is varied, intriguing, and enlightening, but not relevant here.

When Dombey arrived in Cadiz on 22 February 1785, bringing his rich collections, he met with many difficulties which resulted in an enormous loss of time and consequently of living material. In accordance with the agreement, Dombey had split his collections in Peru; he forwarded the Spanish part separately on a ship that never reached its destination. The Spanish government provisionally confiscated the material he brought in, and in the meantime obtained permission from the French court to divide the French part of the collection, which had arrived safely. It is not so much the letter of the rule that was here obeyed as it is the way in which this was all brought about that later raised so much criticism and that resulted in the return to France of a disillusioned Dombey. The most valuable part of his collection had been the living plants which had perished in the customs-houses. On the whole it can be said that the Spanish government was legally correct in what it did; one must have one's doubts, however, of the more human aspects. The part of the material ultimately left to Dombey for France was not released until he promised in writing that he would not publish anything about his travels and discoveries in Spanish America before the return of Ruiz and Pavón. Dombey's manuscripts were therefore doomed to oblivion. It is difficult to say whether the contentions by Deleuze (1804), Smith (1809), and Lasèque (1845) are true, that Ruiz and Pavón made free use of them with hardly any acknowledgment in their own works. If Ruiz and Pavón did so (one could settle this question by comparing the Dombey manuscripts with their books), they were certainly legally entitled to do so, but whether it was ethically justifiable is a different matter.

Dombey found it quite impossible to do anything with the plants that he brought to France. He himself was in difficult financial circumstances. After protracted negotiations he parted with his collection to the director of the *Jardin du Roi,* Georges-Louis Leclerc comte de Buffon [1707-1788], who found him a government pension as well as a grant in aid to pay his debts. The dried plants were then handed over to L'Héritier for publication.

L'Héritier had offered to publish the botanical part of the Dombey collections at his own expense and this offer must have led de Buffon to put the herbarium at the disposal of someone outside the professional circles of the *Jardin du Roi*. Very probably it was L'Héritier, together with Dombey's friend Thouin, who made the arrangement when they realized that the French government was not willing to do very much for the unfortunate Dombey. The arrangement suited both parties: L'Héritier had at last obtained a collection of many new plants from far away regions which satisfied the wishes expressed in his preface to the *Stirpes novae*; the government pension and the payment of debts helped Dombey out of an impossible situation. The details of the arrangement are not clear: little seems to have been put on paper, because of legal difficulties. The result, however, was that L'Héritier received the herbarium for publication and Dombey his stipend.

> "Dombey a enfin son herbier très entier au Cabinet du Roi. Le ministre a chargé M. L'Héritier de le publier de la meme manière que le sien. Jussieu [A. L.] voulait l'avoir ou du moins la moitié mais il en a été empeché d'une manière assez vive, il a l'herbier de Commerson depuis 10 ou 12 ans et a fait déjà 7 ou 8 planches ...". (Dombey has at last his entire herbarium in the King's cabinet. The minister has instructed M. L'Héritier to publish it in the same way as his own. Jussieu wanted to have it or at least half of it, but he has been prevented from having it in a rather emphatic way; he has had the Commerson herbarium for ten or twelve years and has already made seven or eight plates ...). [Broussonet to Banks, 13 Febr. 1786]

This explains why de Jussieu did not succeed in getting the Dombey herbarium. He had made so little progress with the Commerson herbarium that he was not to be entrusted with another one.

Broussonet adds on 7 March 1786 that de Jussieu had done all he could to divide the herbarium and that he had taken seven specimens out of every ten. De Buffon himself had taken a hand in the matter and the herbarium was brought first to the King's cabinet and from there to L'Héritier. This whole arrangement, however, was, strictly speaking, contrary to the conditions on which Dombey had been admitted to the Spanish colonies and certainly contrary to the written promise given by Dombey, most probably under pressure, at Cadiz. As soon as the Spanish government heard about the plans it intervened with the French government to prevent L'Héritier from fulfilling his object. The French government was evidently unwilling to oppose this claim and instructed de Buffon to get the material back from L'Héritier. The latter, however, happened to be at Versailles on the day this decision was taken and, learning of it, hurried home. With help from Broussonet and Redouté, L'Héritier packed the Dombey collections overnight and on 9 September 1786 took them with him by coach for Boulogne, leaving word that he had gone for a holiday at his country-seat Brutelle in Picardy. He took the boat to Dover and had the satisfaction of arriving safely in England with the Dombey treasures.

This move can only be understood when it is realized that the importance attached by all concerned to the Dombey material was based on the undescribed new plants. L'Héritier's intention was to go to England in order to have the time to study the Dombey plants properly, to compare them with the Banks and Smith herbaria, and to publish a *Prodromus* of the Peruvian and Chilean floras based on them. After such a publication (and this is the really revealing sentiment in this romantic affair), L'Héritier was convinced that the Spanish government would lose interest in the matter so that the plants could safely be returned to Paris. The plants were of far greater importance when undescribed than when described: a notion still far from our present-day concept of the importance of type collections.

Sir James Edward Smith, who was in Paris at the moment of L'Héritier's hasty departure for London, had given him an introduction to Dryander, Bank's curator. In a confidential letter to Banks from Paris dated 13 September 1786, he gives the latter some background information and more especially expresses his doubts that the Spaniards will lose interest in the plants after the publication of the intended *Prodromus*. On the contrary, Smith, who had a far more realistic and modern opinion of the value of herbarium specimens than L'Héritier ever had (after all it was he who had acquired the Linnaean herbarium), warns Banks that L'Héritier might be facing trouble and that Banks should try to obtain a duplicate set of the Dombey plants "without such a transaction at present communicated to any mortal." While in London L'Héritier wrote to Banks (20 October 1786) giving the story in his own words. At that time L'Héritier evidently realized already that he might never be able to publish the *Prodromus*, but he adds in conclusion that the Dombey collection would at any rate be saved from the oblivion that threatened those of Commerson and Tournefort. This was a direct reference to A. L. de Jussieu who had been keeping the Commerson plants much too long. It must be said, however, that de Jussieu did rescue the Commerson herbarium from oblivion in his *Genera Plantarum* (August 1789) and that, as we shall see, very little was actually published by L'Héritier of the Dombey material.

It was L'Héritier's intention to remain in London for only three months: in fact he stayed nearly fifteen months, until early December 1787. During that time he was a regular visitor at Soho Square, although in the beginning Banks was furious at L'Héritier mostly because the latter had used his name at the British customs' in importing Dombey's herbarium. Furthermore, L'Héritier had already undertaken the preliminary work for his *Geraniologia* and wanted to add to his manuscript descriptions of Banks's *Gerania*. Banks, knowing that Cavanilles was also working on the genus, suspected foul play. He instructed Dryander to keep a good eye on L'Héritier during the latter's stays at Soho Square, but from the correspondence it is clear that L'Héritier's conduct was always perfectly correct and even exemplary.

No manuscript of L'Héritier's *Prodromus* has ever been seen. He is said to have brought it back to Paris in November 1787, but there is no proof of this. It is not among the L'Héritier papers acquired by A. P. de Candolle and now at Geneva. It seems as if L'Héritier, being in London, contented himself with the description of only a few Dombey plants, but that his attention was drawn mostly to undescribed plants in the Banksian herbarium and to new plants growing at Kew and in other gardens. Several of these plants were described by him during his stay, and the new genera among them received names derived from those of contemporary English botanists. It is this more or less haphazard collection of descriptions and plates of new or imperfectly known plants that L'Héritier ultimately published as his *Sertum Anglicum*. The plates were drawn for him by Sowerby and Redouté, as Wilfrid Blunt relates in his essay in this edition. In

April 1787 L'Héritier had asked Redouté to follow him to London (Hamy 1905, p. 386) and it was here that most of the drawings for the *Sertum Anglicum* were made. L'Héritier seems to have had an instinct for discovering competent draughtsmen, for it was he who made first use of James Sowerby also.

The only plants from the Dombey herbarium described by L'Héritier while he was in London are the few incorporated in the *Sertum Anglicum* (*e.g., Amaryllis maculata,* p. 10, of which the type is at Paris). Most of the new species and genera were later described by Ruiz and Pavón, who, after all, had the Dombey material at their disposal in addition to their own collections.

L'Héritier returned to Paris early in December 1787 and resumed his correspondence with Banks on 24 December. He winds up the Dombey affair as follows:

> "J'espere qu'on me laissera tranquilement achever la besogne de Dombey. Qui que ce soit icy ne se doute du principal objet de mon voyage à Londres, à l'exception de quelques amis qui etoient dans mon secret. M. de Buffon ne pensant en ce moment qu'à se defendre contre la mort, Dombey ainsi que moi pourrions bien être oubliés". (I hope that I will be left to finish quietly with the Dombey affair. Nobody here has even an inkling of the main object of my London trip, with the exception of some friends who shared my secret. Since M. de Buffon at this moment has to think only of defending himself against death, Dombey as well as myself may well be forgotten).

De Buffon actually died somewhat later (16 April 1788), but at this time he was evidently no longer in a position to reclaim the material. The Dombey herbarium came back to L'Héritier in Paris in February 1788, and on 30 April 1788 he informs Banks that Dombey is at Paris and that together they are going to study his herbarium in great detail. He says the same in a letter to Dryander dated 14 May 1788. Duplicates were duly sent to Banks in the course of 1788, and since no real publication took place the Spanish botanists were free to go ahead with their own work, based mainly on their own material and annotations, but undoubtedly also to some extent on that of the unfortunate Dombey.

L'Héritier kept the plants and note-books until his death. He reaffirmed as late as 11 December 1797 his intention to publish on this collection (Hamy 1905, p. 392, Déhérain 1907) in a letter to the Professors of the Muséum d'Histoire naturelle who had several times asked for the return of the material. The plants and manuscripts were sent to the Muséum on 24 January 1801 by his children (Hamy 1905, p. 394).

Fate remained unkind towards Joseph Dombey. In May 1794 he perished in a prison on the island of Montserrat, after another series of adventures for an account of which this is not the proper place. The affair was characteristic of the tragic life of Dombey, the energetic and gay explorer, of whom as a young man Deleuze (1804) said: "le lendemain étoit pour lui un avenir éloigné," and of whom one can only say that rarely has a capable man met with so many tragic misfortunes.

THE YEAR OF UNABATED ACTIVITY: 1788

L'Héritier resumed his usual routine after his return from England in December 1787. He continued to work at the *Jardin du Roi* and its herbaria, especially on the *Geraniologia*. While studying the Tournefort and Vaillant herbaria he writes to Banks (24 December 1787) complaining about the difficulty of distinguishing between the various species, which he could not compare because some were in England and others in France, all dispersed. The publication of the *Stirpes novae* was resumed, the fourth fascicle appearing in March 1788. Even earlier L'Héritier had begun one of his bibliographically most puzzling activities. Soon after his return from England he started the publication of a series of "dissertations" which are exceedingly rare. They are mostly undated but were all probably published between December 1787 and January 1789. Cuvier (1801) relates that only five copies of each were printed, but at present only two sets are known to exist, one at the British Museum and one at Geneva. Cuvier adds that L'Héritier distributed them to different persons so that none of them would ever possess a complete set. This was not true of Banks, who got a complete or almost complete set. The Geneva set is the one De Candolle obtained after L'Héritier's death and is probably that retained by L'Héritier himself. The first dissertation, *Louichea,* was published late in December 1787. It consists simply of a title-page carrying the name of the genus, followed by a plate and two pages of text. The dissertation is not dated. It is of the same size as the *Stirpes novae,* in which it was included later as plate 65 and pages 135-136 in the sixth fascicle (September 1791). *Louichea* was named after René-Louiche Desfontaines (1750-1823) one of the few professional botanists in Paris with whom L'Héritier entertained good relations, and who also belonged to the group of Malesherbes and Jean-Jacques Rousseau. Desfontaines had just (1786) succeeded Lemonnier as professor of botany, an appointment in which L'Héritier had also been instrumental. In his letter to Banks of 31 December 1787 L'Héritier presents him with a copy, saying "Voicy un petit echantillon du Louichea cervina plante d'Arabie que je viens de publier separement pour essaier les presses de Didot le Je." (I enclose a specimen of *Louichea cervina,* a plant from Arabia, which I have just published separately to try out the presses of Didot the younger). This is not quite the same explanation as that given by Cuvier, who says that L'Héritier was driven to do this by excessive bibliomania. Other dissertations followed: *Michauxia* and *Virgilia* of which L'Héritier says, in a letter to Dryander dated 29 July 1788, that two "editions" had been published. These dissertations are just as short as the earlier *Louichea,* but were not republished in the *Stirpes novae.* While these two undated treatises evidently appeared after *Louichea* and before 29 July, two others appeared in the second half of 1788, *Buchozia* and *Hymenopappus.*

A treatise on *Kakile,* dated 1788 (Pritzel 5271), was never really published. Two copies of it are known to exist (at the Paris Muséum d'Histoire naturelle, and at the Conservatoire botanique at Geneva) but these are evidently proof-sheets which cannot be regarded as effectively published. The same holds for some plates without text preserved at Geneva.

In his correspondence with Banks, on 2 June 1788, in an additional note dated 3 July,

L'Héritier reveals an interesting side of his character when he gives the reasons for the establishment of his new genus *Buchozia*. "Do not suspect me of trying to prostitute Botany by means of the name *Buchozia*, it is more to take revenge." He explains that the species in question (*Lycium foetidum* L.f.) had a bad odor and is therefore excellently suited for the purpose. Botany had to "take revenge" because Pierre-Joseph Buc'hoz [1731-1807], after whom the plant had been called, indiscriminately compiled a great number of rather useless botanical books, freely using the works of others.

L'Héritier was very active in enlarging his library in the years that immediately followed his stay in England. His library was already remarkable before 1786, but in the house at Soho Square he had seen a real scholar's library, open to all visitors. It became his ambition to build up a library like that. He was certainly successful in doing this, as is shown by the remarkable catalogue of his books which was first published by Debure in 1802, and again in 1805 when they were sold. L'Héritier could not add much to the library after he had lost his fortune during the revolution, but he kept it intact, and always admitted botanists who wanted to consult it. During the revolutionary years the public collections were not always open, but L'Héritier's books were always available for consultation. At his death his library included nearly 8,000 titles, most of them on natural history. He also possessed a remarkable collection of travel-books. The library was first put on sale on 10 May 1802; the bookseller Mérigot bought it as a whole in the hope of selling it to another agency (probably the Muséum d'Histoire naturelle) so that it might be kept intact. The professors at the Muséum tried in vain to convince the government that this unique private library, second only in its field to that of Banks, should be bought as a whole but no satisfactory arrangement with the heirs was reached (Hamy 1905, p. 395). Mérigot did not find another buyer and he was obliged to sell this wonderful library in an open auction and saw it dispersed in August 1805.

In the course of 1788 L'Héritier developed a lively correspondence with Dryander ("*L'Héritier corr.*") who was preparing the text for the first edition of W. Aiton's *Hortus Kewensis*. Dryander sent sheets of the *Hortus Kewensis* to L'Héritier who in turn provided Dryander with all the necessary details of his planned *Sertum Anglicum*. This is the reason that so many plants from the *Sertum Anglicum* are correctly referred to by Dryander in the *Hortus Kewensis*, notwithstanding that the printing of the latter book had been started (in the first half of 1788) long before the first fascicle of the *Sertum Anglicum* became available. In many instances L'Héritier asks for Dryander's advice whether or not to establish a particular genus, and the tone of the letters is always most cordial. Dryander is informed for the first time by L'Héritier of his plan to publish the *Sertum* in a letter dated 20 April 1788:

"Je comptois publier dans un ouvrage particulier les plantes les plus rares que j'ai fait dessiner en Angleterre sous le titre de *Sertum anglicum*. Comme il seroit trop long d'attendre que le tout fut gravé, et pour profiter d'autant mieux de votre *hortus Kewensis* je vais publier les deux ou trois premières qui sont gravées et en tete je donnerai un Prodromus de tout l'ouvrage avec des noms triviaux [et] differentia specifica pour chaque espece. Ce prodrome qui contiendra en même tems l'etablissement des nouveaux genres une fois publié les planches paroitront successivement deux à deux ou trois à trois sans inconvenient. Voicy la liste de ce que contiendra ce *Sertum anglicum*." [There follows a list of the first 26 planned plates, of which only the first seven agree with the actually published plates.] "Il faudra que tous les nouveaux genres de ce Cahier ne portent pas d'autres noms que ceux de Botanistes anglois, pour cadrer d'autant mieux avec le titre."

(I hoped to publish in a special work the rarest plants of which I had drawings made in England, under the title *Sertum Anglicum*. Because it would take too long to wait until everything was engraved, and in order to profit better by your *Hortus Kewensis*, I am going to publish the first two or three [plates] that have been engraved and preceding them I will give a *prodromus* of the entire work with the trivial names and the specific differences for each species. This *prodromus* will contain at the same time the establishment of the new genera; as soon as it is published the plates will appear successively two by two or three by three without any difficulty. Here is the list of the contents of the *Sertum Anglicum* … . All new genera of this fascicle must not bear any other names but those of English botanists, in order to agree better with the title.)

L'Héritier did not quite fulfill his promise to dedicate all his new genera to English botanists. Of the thirteen new generic names, seven are derived from names of English botanists. They are *Boltonia, Dicksonia, Lightfootia, Pitcairnia, Relhania, Stokesia,* and *Witheringia*.

The names *Banksia, Dryandra,* and *Smithia* had already been used by others, so that L'Héritier was not in a position to honor those who had received him so well during his stay in London.

JAMES B. BOLTON (ca. 1740?-1799) published, among other things, on British ferns and fungi, and co-operated with Withering and Relhan. In addition, he was an outstanding British botanical artist of that time.

JAMES DICKSON (1738-1822), a nurseryman and botanist, issued fascicles of British cryptogams and phanerogams.

THE REV. JOHN LIGHTFOOT (1735-1788) published a *Flora Scotica* (1777-1778). He travelled through Scotland in 1772 and (with Banks) through Wales in 1773.

WILLIAM PITCAIRN (1711-1791) was a physician who kept a botanic garden at Islington at the time of L'Héritier's visit.

THE REV. RICHARD RELHAN (1754-1823) published a *Flora Cantabrigiensis* from 1785 to 1793.

JONATHAN STOKES (1755-1831) was a physician and amateur botanist who drew plates for Withering's publications.

WILLIAM WITHERING (1741-1799), was a physician in Birmingham at the time of L'Héritier's visit. He published the *Botanical arrangement of all the vegetables naturally growing in Great Britain* … (1776).

In his subsequent letters L'Héritier practically transcribes the text of his *Synopsis operis,* although in a different order, and adding short notes in French which help to understand his way of working. Under his *Celastrus octogonus,* for instance, which was described from a Dombey specimen from Peru, he adds: "Je vous envoie un echantillon de cette plante qui est à Kew pourque vous la reconnoissiez …" (22 June 1788 L'Héritier to Dryander) (I am sending you a specimen of this plant which is at Kew in order that you may recognize it). Under the next species, *Celastrus undulatus,* he mentions also in the printed text that although he knew the plant from a Commerson specimen in the Paris garden, he had seen the plant also in England in the garden of James Lee.

A publication for which L'Héritier did much spade-work but which was never realized was his *Solana aliquot rariora,* of which he gives ample details in his letters to Dryander. The latter used the details of his treatment of *Solanum* in volume one of Aiton's *Hortus Kewensis,* using the designation *"L'Hérit. solan. tab.* " On p. xxi of the *Hortus Kewensis* this book is listed as "not yet published." It never was.

On 20 July 1788 L'Héritier thanks Dryander for the first sheets of the *Hortus Kewensis.* In return he sends him, on 8 August 1788, the first three sheets of the *Sertum.* He also sends Dryander with that same letter the drawing of *Amaryllis spiralis* (reproduced in this edition on p. *lxiv*) with a request to compare it with other material.

A very interesting place in this correspondence is that in which L'Héritier explains to Dryander (1 September 1788) which rules guide him in the choice of his names and in the application of names given by others. This passage is partly quoted also by Britten and Woodward (1905) but it is sufficiently important to be included in this record.

> "Vous me faites une guerre impitoyable pour les changemens de noms. Il est peut-être un peu trop vague de s'en tenir toujours au premier nom imprimé. On courroit risque d'en adopter de trop mauvais, et cela conte lorsqu'on sent la possibilité d'en donner un bon. Je ne changerai point les noms donnés dans des ouvrages d'une certaine consequence, en un mot dans ceux qui marquent et comptent en Botanique. Mais pour ceux qui ne se trouvent inserés que dans des dissertations, ou memoires academiques, je pense qu'on peut sans consequence les changer, non pour le plaisir de changer, mais si l'on trouve occasion d'en substituer un meilleur. Par exemple *Koelreuteria.* Vous conviendrez que ce nom etoit ignoré dans les Jardins. J'ai été tenté d'appeler ce genre *Laxmannia* et s'il ne s'en trouvoit pas un dejà dans forster [J. R. et G. Forster, *Char. gen.* 93. 1776] je l'eus certainement fait. Si d'ailleurs ce genre eut eté dedié par flatterie ou autrement à quelqu'un qui en fut indigne, j'avoue que je n'aurois pas hesité à le changer, sauf à le voir adopter ou rejetter par ceux qui m'auroient suivi. Pour les noms triviaux, voicy mon opinion. Dans les genres nouveaux qui ne contiennent qu'un espèce le nom trivial me paroit être celui qui rapproche ce genre du genre le plus voisin. Cela presente aussitôt une idée utile. En general quel devroit être le nom trivial pour être le meilleur possible? Il faudroit qu'il distingue l'espece [des] autres du même genre, ou au moins qu'il ne convient qu'a une seule espece ..."

(You quarrel with me pitilessly over the name-changes. It is perhaps a bit too vague to accept always the first name that was printed. One runs the risk of adopting very bad ones, and this is of importance when one recognizes the possibility of giving a good one. I do not change the names given in works of a certain importance, in one word those that have a standing in botany. But with regard to those published only in dissertations or academic memoirs, I think that one can change them without difficulty, not for the pleasure of changing, but only if one has the opportunity of giving a better one. Take for instance *Koelreuteria.* You will agree that this name was unknown in the gardens. I have been tempted to call the genus *Laxmannia* and, if there had not already been one in Forster, I should certainly have done so. If on the other hand this genus had been dedicated out of flattery or otherwise to one who was not worth it, I confess that I should not have hesitated to change it, and see it adopted or rejected by those who would come after me. For the trivial names here is my opinion. In new genera which contain a single species, the trivial name seems to me to be the one which compares the genus with the nearest allied genus. This gives at once a useful idea. In general what should the trivial name be in order to be the best possible one? It would be necessary for it to distinguish the species from the others of the same genus, or at least to be applicable only to a single species ...)

On 21 September 1788 L'Héritier asks Dryander to send him a suitable motto for the *Sertum Anglicum* referring to the English gardens or nurserymen. Dryander sent him the lines from Thomson's *Seasons* reproduced on the verso of L'Héritier's introduction to the reader. L'Héritier must have been struck by the lines "[where] Liberty abroad walks, unconfin'd, even to thy farthest cotes, and scatters plenty with unsparing hand" because of their joint application to English horticulture and politics both of which he held in very high regard.

From another letter (2 October 1788) to Dryander it is clear that the work was not planned beyond the *Dicksonia,* as actually scheduled in the *synopsis operis.* The plate for *Dicksonia* (*t. 43*) was to be the last one, and was to be drawn by Sowerby. The actual volume remained unfinished: plates 35-43 were never published, and the special treatment of the illustrated species, such as is given for *Witheringia solanacea* and *Chloranthus inconspicuus* and included in the first fascicle, was never continued because of the revolution.

THE TURBULENT YEARS: 1789-1794

The *Sertum Anglicum* (part 1), the fifth installment of the *Stirpes novae,* and L'Héritier's treatise on *Cornus* were all published very early in 1789. The fifth fascicle of the *Stirpes* (with the date 1785 on the title-page) dealt with a number of Malvaceae, mainly of the genus *Sida* on which the abbé Antonio José Cavanilles (1754-1804) had been publishing in his *Dissertationes* between 1785 and 1788. The antedating of L'Héritier's fifth fascicle aroused the anger of the abbé who, not without reason, was afraid that by this procedure some names of L'Héritier would be given precedence over some of his own which had actually been published considerably earlier. Cavanilles rushed into print in the *Journal de Paris* (20 February 1789, no. 51) and later also in the famous *Observations sur la Physique* (March 1789) to set things right. L'Héritier answered (also in the *Journal de Paris,* 4 March 1789, no. 63, and in the *Observations sur la Physique* of March 1789), and a little paper war developed. The details of this rather acrimonious battle are unimportant. It is evident that the antedating of L'Héritier's publications (he did this with the fascicles of his *Stirpes* and with his later *Geraniologia*) was wrong. This does not mean, however, that it was L'Héritier's intention to claim false priority. On the contrary there is every reason to believe that this strange and undesirable practice sprung from L'Héritier's desire to adhere to his original scheme of publication.

> "M. Cavanilles trouvera bon que je remplisse ma tâche envers le public. En commençant mes *Stirpes novae,* j'ai promis quatre fascicules par année. Mon séjour en Angleterre a interrompu mes livraisons mais la besogne n'a pas moins été faite et disposée, et j'espère m'acquitter peu à peu. Mon sixième fascicule, qui est imprimé [*sic* March 1789] est pareillement daté de 1785 …". [see also *Mag. Bot. Roemer & Usteri* 7: 72. 1790]. (M. Cavanilles will approve my fulfilling my duties to the public. When I started my *Stirpes novae,* I promised four fascicles per year. My stay in England has interrupted the delivery but the work has none the less been done and finished, and I hope to acquit myself little by little. My sixth fascicle, which is printed, is likewise dated 1785 …).

L'Héritier could not publish as quickly as he wanted, not even when financing the publications himself, and there is every reason to believe that much, though not all, of the copy was ready long before publication. L'Héritier did not attach great value to priority, as has been shown above, and it would be wrong to suppose that this undesirable practice sprang from equally undesirable motives. The result, however, was certainly regrettable, although there is not much difficulty in dating the publications. They were all promptly reviewed and the discrepancy between the title-page dates and those of actual publication was repeatedly mentioned by reviewers and openly accepted by the author.

Cornus, also dated 1788, was published in the beginning of 1789, actually either in January or in February. We know that on 29 December 1788 the work had not yet been printed, because L'Héritier says so in a letter to Dryander, and that on 21 February 1789 it had been published according to a review in the *Obs. Phys. Hist. Nat. Paris* 34: 155 (1789; date of censor 21 February). The book consists of the treatment of six species of *Cornus,* illustrated by large plates after the manner of the *Stirpes novae.* It is of little taxonomic importance because all species had been previously described. Three of the plates are by P.-J. Redouté.

The political events in late 1788 and early 1789 give L'Héritier cause for comment in his letters to English botanists. For a long time he shows practically no emotion at all, although he does not leave any doubt about his opinion that far-reaching reforms, even of a revolutionary character, are desirable and forthcoming. The descriptions by L'Héritier of the momentous events of 1789 and later years make fascinating reading, not the least because of their great impartiality and because of the objective stand which they always take. The correct and straightforward magistrate presents himself in these letters, and they form a strange mixture of political reporting and botanical discussion. In April 1789 L'Héritier is appointed elector for the new national assembly. He does not want to become a deputy but this business of simply nominating the deputies takes four weeks of his time which he considers as lost, "just as if I had been confined to my bed." He rather doubts whether all this ado will lead to something, but thinks that the mountain has given birth to a mouse. On 16 July 1789 he writes a moving letter to Banks describing the events of the last four days ("they seem to have been years") in great detail and with great fairness. The passage is too long to be transcribed here, and falls outside the scope of this introduction. It is practically the only document we know in which L'Héritier shows considerable emotion, and in which the sensitive man shows himself rather than the righteous magistrate or the fanatic amateur botanist. The subsequent letters show his disappointment over the atrocities and the many absurdities of the revolution. It was not the first nor the last time that a man with high human ideals felt himself betrayed when his ideals began to be realized. In the course of the next years L'Héritier loses nearly all his possessions, as did so many of the other well-to-do magistrates. His popularity as a judge, however, is shown by the respectful tributes paid to him by the various revolutionary committees and councils. In October 1789 he is appointed commander of the battalion of the National Guard (500-700 men) raised by the district in which he lived (St. Nicolas des Champs), after having refused an appointment as deputy of his "commune." As such he did what he could to moderate the revolutionary activities and to prevent wanton murder. His battalion was among the troops of the National Guard that went to Versailles during the October riots which ended with the bizarre transfer of the king to Paris. L'Héritier's battalion was the one that stopped the murder by the mob of the king's bodyguard. L'Héritier was also involved in some of the strange baker's incidents well known from those days. "Depuis la revolution, je suis resigné à être pendu, massacré, pillé ... pourvu que nous puissions sauver notre chere Patrie" (letter to Banks 29 October 1789). (Since the revolution I have resigned myself to being hung, murdered or plundered ... if only we can save our dear country.) It is clear that L'Héritier took part in what has been called the "bourgeois revolution" and not in the "popular revolution" (Lefebvre 1962). He tried from the beginning to promote certain reforms and was completely convinced as early as 1787 or even 1786 that the *ancien régime* was doomed. The atrocities of the popular revolution, however, were a nightmare to him.

Later, in the beginning of 1790 when events were less tumultuous, L'Héritier had new hopes, although his duties as commandant took nearly all his time and he did but little botanical work. In May 1790 he informed Banks that all botanists had embraced the good cause: Jussieu was *Lieutenant de maire*. Broussonet secretary of the municipality, Thouin representative of the *commune*, he himself commander of a battalion, and Lamarck only a private soldier. The Constituent Assembly appointed L'Héritier judge at the tribunal of the second arrondissement in the course of 1790, one of the very few magistrates of the *ancien régime* deemed worthy of reappointment.

The Academy of Sciences was still functioning and on 17 May 1790 L'Héritier was elected associate member in the place of Lamarck who became *pensionnaire* (full member with full payment). Among the other candidates were Louis-Claude-Marie Richard (1754-1821), Palisot de Beauvois (1752-1820), Jacques-Julien Houton de la Billardière (1755-1834), all younger than L'Héritier. Jussieu, Lamarck, and Adanson voted against L'Héritier, all for different reasons. In L'Héritier's time new members were first appointed as associate members and could become full members only if there was a vacancy. The numbers of both associate and full members were fixed, so that new elections took place only when a vacancy occurred. Because of his many duties at the town hall and with his battalion, L'Héritier could attend only relatively few of the sessions in the period 1790-1793: his presence is indicated only in about half of them. In 1791 he read before the Academy two memoirs, which have not been published; one on *Hemitomus* and another on *Podocarpus*. The Academy of Sciences was abolished on 14 August 1793, together with the other Academies, and they remained closed until their reinstatement in 1795.

In that same month of May 1790, L'Héritier published the second part of his *Sertum Anglicum,* consisting only of ten plates (*iii-xii*) without text. He mentions the publication on 24 May 1790 in a letter to J. E. Smith, and states without comment that it does not contain any discussions. The volume is so thin that he awaits the publication of his sixth part of the *Stirpes novae* before sending it. This sixth part, however, was evidently held up considerably: it appeared not earlier than 30 September 1791 (letter to J. E. Smith of 25 September 1791). On 20 June 1790 L'Héritier informs Banks of the decree by the National Assembly, issued the previous night, which abolished the use of all titles, coats of arms, liveries, and the like. He is of the opinion that this would have come naturally, but that this precipitous action will now give rise to renewed insults to the aristocrats from the people. He signs (with a rare spark of humor): "L'Héritier, ni comte ni Marquis." L'Héritier's family belonged to the lowest gentry only and the "seignior of Brutelle" had already been dropped for quite some time.

The year 1791 saw also the publication of two memoirs in the *Transactions of the Linnean Society* (vol. 1), and in April 1792 L'Héritier succeeded at last in bringing out his *Geraniologia* (title-page date 1787-88). He had been working on this book during his stay in London in 1786 and 1787, and also later at irregular intervals, but here again the French revolution intervened. Many of the plates had been drawn, but we may conclude that there was no money left to bring out the text. The *Geraniologia* as published is simply a collection of forty-four plates of which thirty-one were by Redouté and six by Sowerby. The history of this book would merit a treatise of its own, the more so since proofs of a kind of "Compendium" as well as part of the manuscript of the text have been preserved at Geneva.

In this same month (April 1792) L'Héritier published the third part of the *Sertum Anglicum,* again consisting of plates only (*tt. xiii-xxiv, xv bis*). Copies of it were sent to Smith together with the *Geraniologia* on 9 April 1792. The last part (*tt. xxv-xxxiv*) came out later that year, but it is not known precisely at what date. Like his other publications, the *Sertum Anglicum* got stuck in the darkest period of the French revolution, which lasted from September 1792 until 27 July 1794, (9 thermidor an 2) the fall of Robespierre.

We know very little of L'Héritier's activities during the reign of terror. The correspondence with English botanists was interrupted in September 1792 and there are only a few documents from that period that have a bearing on L'Héritier, none of which gives much useful information. In 1793 he lost his position at the *Cour des Aides* and began the most obscure year of his life. He had lost his fortune and the circumstances were unfavorable for the continuation of his publications. In this period he took a position in a kind of welfare organization and somehow escaped from the general persecution of people of his sort.

De Candolle (1834) relates that L'Héritier was imprisoned "par suite d'une basse vengeance" (because of a mean revenge) and in grave danger of being executed. Desfontaines and Thouin intervened and got his release on the pretext that L'Héritier still had to describe the Dombey collections. De Candolle concludes that by means of this ruse, L'Héritier was saved from a death that seemed inevitable. It is a pity that the story is apocryphal, no confirmation of it having been found; if true it may be regarded as a just reward for what L'Héritier had done previously for both Dombey and Desfontaines.

In the summer of the year 1794 L'Héritier lost his wife, and was left with the problem of educating his five children. His relations with his eldest son, Jacques, seem to have been already rather difficult at this time; the other children were considerably younger. The eldest son soon left the parental home, the eldest daughter, Marie, was sent to live with another family, and the three youngest children, one boy, Charles, and two girls, Adelaïde and Rose, were probably taken care of by L'Héritier himself and his servants. The youngest girl, Rose, was only one or two years old; she died at the age of ninety-nine in 1892.

AFTERMATH AND THE END: 1794-1800

As soon as France could breathe again, after "thermidor," L'Héritier could face a new life. He was appointed *commis* at the new ministry of justice, very probably a rather modest position. Deprived of his fortune and faced with the difficulty of giving his children a proper education, he must have found the years 1794 and 1795 difficult. There is a story (by Cuvier) that during these years, L'Héritier compiled a *Flore de la Place Vendôme*, simply by collecting in Paris, in the vicinity of the ministry at which he worked, all the plants growing on the walls, between the stones of the pavement, etc. He may have mentioned this activity later to Cuvier, and L'Héritier will have remained the ardent botanist he was in these years too, but this story also must remain apocryphal, since it has been impossible to find confirmation.

In these years L'Héritier was a member of the *Commission d'Agriculture et des Arts*, a committee set up by the republican government to deal with certain specific questions. Together with the famous Claude-Louis Berthollet [1748-1822] and the then still young writer Pierre-François Tissot [1768-1854], L'Héritier published three memoirs on agricultural subjects. The first is a report on marshes and ponds ("étangs") dealing with their drainage or reclamation in order to provide the rural economy with more arable land (130 pages, dated 5 nivôse de l'an 3e, 25 December 1794). The second report, undated, deals with the extraction of oil from beech-nuts (*Extraction de l'huile de Faîne*) (48 pp.). The third, also undated, discusses the conservation and use of potatoes (38 pp.). Since Tissot was a member of this Committee only in the first half of 1794, and from October 1794 until April 1795 these memoirs must date from those periods. We encounter L'Héritier here in his original role of applied botanist. The pamphlets are very rare, but copies are preserved at the Bibliothèque nationale and the Muséum d'Histoire naturelle in Paris.

One curious manuscript by L'Héritier, written some time after the revolution but undated, should be mentioned again here. It is his unpublished memoir on *Redoutea*, in which he expressed his warm appreciation for Redouté so nicely. The description of the genus is followed by a long discussion of its place in the various methods of classification and it is here that we find the only place where the more mature L'Héritier gives an opinion on the natural system. The discussion shows clearly that this side of taxonomy was not his strongest. After explaining at some length the greater convenience of classification by the Linnaean sexual system, L'Héritier surprisingly makes the statement that "the true natural method will be, as in the works of Adanson and de Jussieu, that taking into account all the characteristics of the plants and combining all the links between their parts." He develops this theme metaphorically in a rather hazy way, but the essential point is that he here clearly recognizes the possibility of a natural system, though perhaps not for the purposes of classification.

On 22 August 1795 (5 fructidor, an 3) the Academies came to life again united in the *Institut national des Sciences et des Arts,* often referred to as the *Institut.* The former *Académie des Sciences* became the *Première Classe de l'Institut national.* L'Héritier became a *membre résidant* (another term for full membership) of the botany section on 13 December 1795. This must have eased his circumstances; apart from the status that it gave him the modest salary that went with the appointment must have come as a great relief. L'Héritier was a good member: of the 335 meetings held between his appointment in December 1795 and his death in August 1800 he missed only 18: a remarkable achievement. His activities at the academy are of limited interest.

On 21 March 1796 (1 germinal, an 4) L'Héritier read a memoir before the Institute dealing with the effects of the cold period of 26 February to 10 March 1796 on various cultivated plants, and more especially on the pears. In this memoir (L'Héritier 1798) we find again some indication of a sense of humor when he says that instead of being destroyed by the cold with the flowerbuds of the pears, noxious insects survived the cold period excellently. Some of these insects had been declared noxious by official republican decree, but, says L'Héritier, unless the entomologists do something about it, the insects will survive the republican laws just as they survived the decrees of previous parliaments and the thunderbolts from the Vatican.

L'Héritier was also a member of an academy committee studying the then rather wide-spread elm-disease.

The last botanical publication known to us, is his *Mémoire sur un nouveau genre de plants appelé Cadia,* which appeared in the *Magasin encyclopédique* in 1795. Separately paged reprints of this publication (14 pp.) exist.

We thus find that notwithstanding his easier circumstances, L'Héritier did not produce anything of importance after the terror of 1792-1794. His time seems to have been taken fully by his duties at the ministry of Justice (he had become chief secretary of the ministry and he was also a judge at the *tribunal d'appel*) and by the ordinary affairs of the academy. Nothing is known of any attempts to complete his works. After all, none of his major works, the *Stirpes novae,* the *Sertum Anglicum,* and the *Geraniologia* had been properly finished. They had been published by Didot at L'Héritier's expense, as is shown from the way L'Héritier invoiced other botanists to whom he sent copies. But was the loss of fortune the only reason? At his death he was again a relatively wealthy man, as is evident from the description of his estate (*Archives Seine*). Would it not have been possible to have found another agency of publisher willing to finish the job? Probably not. The times were still very difficult.

We have only one good contemporary account of L'Héritier's latest years, that given by Augustin-Pyramus De Candolle (1778-1841) in his *Mémoires et Souvenirs* (1862). L'Héritier had asked Redouté to begin drawings of a great number of succulent plants, possibly for a future publication, but nothing came of it until Redouté, through Desfontaines, got in touch with De Candolle. Out of this grew the publication of the famous *Historia plantarum succulentarum* by De Candolle and Redouté.

De Candolle tells that L'Héritier, after having been ruined financially by the revolution, had accepted this modest position at the ministry of justice, but that he did very little botany in those days (1798-1800). He still had his great library, and offered the use of it to the young Swiss botanist. "He was a dry man, cold in appearance, actually passionate, acrimonious, and sarcastic in conversation, given to a kind of predilection for small intrigues, a declared enemy of de Jussieu, de Lamarck, and even of the new methods, but always doing for me acts of kindness for which I was grateful."

The bookseller Garnery bought from the estate L'Héritier's herbarium, manuscripts, and unpublished drawings and plates, with the intention of publishing at least the last two installments of the *Stirpes novae,* the seventh containing *Spartium, Genista,* and *Cytisus,* and the eighth which was to have contained *Solanum* (probably the text for the unpublished *Solana aliquot rariora*). Garnery owed a sum of 1,500 francs to De Candolle and gave him L'Héritier's extensive herbarium (8,000 species), as well as the manuscripts, on the understanding that he would make the two installments ready for the press. De Candolle states that he was very happy with the rich herbarium, but that the publication of the L'Héritier manuscripts would have been a considerable work which would have taken several years of his life "sans grande utilité." De Candolle further states that Garnery was fortunately very lax and did not even publish the parts he had made ready for the press, and that he therefore easily escaped from an obligation undertaken in his enthusiasm to get hold of the herbarium. He evidently did not care very much about the manuscripts of his "ancien protecteur," he was too young perhaps to feel a debt of gratitude, and wanted to go ahead with his own work. Through this chain of events, L'Héritier's work remained unfinished after his death, abruptly broken off by the events of the French revolution, just as L'Héritier's life was abruptly broken off in the late hours of 16 August 1800.

The end came, suddenly and horribly, on this summer evening. L'Héritier had been working at the institute and returned home rather late. Near his house he was attacked and murdered.

The murder has never been clarified. It created an enormous impression, for even after so many years, L'Héritier was widely known as the judge from the *Cour des Aides.* No reports were ever published, and those in the archives of the Paris police do not contain further details. Of the biographers it is J. E. Smith alone who more or less hints at the possibility that L'Héritier was murdered by his eldest son, who had caused him many difficulties. This son, Jacques, died in 1801; after his father's death he was away from Paris for a considerable time.

L'Héritier's body was buried in the garden of his last Paris house, (rue des Amandiers, now rue du Chemin Vert), in the present 11th arrondissement. On 10 March 1812 the body was transferred to the nearby Père-Lachaise cemetery (*Cimetière de l'est*).

George Cuvier read a sympathetic and moving account of his friend's life before the *Institut* on 5 April 1801 (15 germinal, an 9). Through it sounds the emotion caused by the loss of this eager botanist and just man who had sacrificed so much for his science and his vocation as a magistrate, and whose great objects in life had remained unfulfilled.

THE PUBLICATION OF THE SERTUM ANGLICUM

The *Sertum Anglicum* consists of thirty-six pages of text and thirty-five plates (numbered 1-15, 15 bis, 16-34). It was published in four installments, of which the first contained all the text. For purposes of priority, only the date of the first installment is of importance because the valid publication of the new names contained in the work was effected in the text.

The text consists of a *Synopsis operis* of thirty-two pages and of two more detailed descriptions of the plants illustrated by the first two plates. In this *Synopsis* all plants, of which illustrations were intended, forty-four are briefly described. In addition a number of other species are treated which belong to the same genera as those illustrated. Of the planned forty-four plates only thirty-five were actually published. The plates were to be accompanied by special text as in the *Stirpes novae,* but because of the revolution and the subsequent loss of L'Héritier's fortune these descriptions were never published, except the first two.

The special text for the plates 3-34 (including pl. 15 *bis*), the unpublished plates 35-43, as well as the original manuscript of the published part, have not been found among the L'Héritier papers obtained by A. P. De Candolle and now at Geneva. However, a rough first draft of the text for many of the plates as well as for parts of the *Synopsis* is preserved in manuscript at the Geneva *Conservatoire botanique.* The only original drawings known at this time are the three reproduced in this edition and part of the drawing for *t. 17* (originals of *tt. 14* and *15-bis* are at the Hunt Botanical Library, and for *tt. 13* and *17* at the British Museum, Natural History). Drawings by Redouté of the plants depicted on *tt. 11, 16,* and *20* are preserved at the Paris *Muséum d'Histoire naturelle.*

It is questionable whether the drawings for plates 35-42 were ever made. From a letter to Dryander dated 2 October 1788 we know that by then a drawing for plate 43 had been made, but that Sowerby was still to be asked to provide a drawing of *Dicksonia culcita* which was to become plate 44.

The plates were often struck off as soon as they had been engraved. Some of the sheets may have been sent by L'Héritier to his friends abroad, but this haphazard distribution of single plates cannot be taken (and was certainly not so intended) as effective publication of the new names they bore.

In his correspondence L'Héritier says several times (*e.g.,* in his letter to Banks dated 11 December 1788) that 350 copies were made, of which fifty were on so-called *papier vélin,* the others on ordinary rag paper, called *papier châpelet,* which is in this case unmarked French white laid paper provided with normal chain-lines. The maker of the ordinary rag-paper is unknown. The *papier vélin* is wove paper, characterised by the absence of chain-lines. Several years before the printing of this work began, the Didot firm had already experimented with this probably rather expensive type of paper (possibly from their own mill). The only copy printed on *papier vélin* known to us, of the fifty mentioned by "L'Héritier" is the one at the *Bibliothèque nationale* in Paris. It is larger than the ordinary paper edition (which is usually 53.3 × 36.6 cm), so much larger that the plates, which are folded in the edition on ordinary paper, are here inserted unfolded. The size of the folded plates in the ordinary edition may be up to 70.4 × 52.5 cm, the leaves of the *papier vélin* edition are about 60.0 × 44.0 cm. Neither the ordinary edition nor that on *papier vélin* are "folio" as is so often stated; there are some folio plates (the folded ones) in the ordinary edition but the text and the majority of the plates are *carré* broadsheet, as is evident from the direction of the chain-lines which run horizontally across the leaf, thus indicating that the top of the leaf was indeed the shorter side as manufactured. Furthermore, there are pin-holes in the middle of the inner and outer margins of each leaf of text. These are from the "points" of the tympan which were used to ensure that the leaf was centred on the plates in the same way for the printing of each side so that the printed surface of one side would correspond in register with the printed surface of the other side. In some copies [two at the University of California, Berkeley, one at the National Agricultural Library, Washington, D. C.] there exists another leaf, a half-title to the fourth fascicle, which lists the plates in that fascicle (25-34). There is no date on it. It differs from the text leaves in that it is in folio, the chain lines running vertically, and it bears a watermark "B [Heart] R F" which does not appear elsewhere in the work. The conjugate leaf is absent.

It remains doubtful whether 350 copies were struck off. We have been able to trace only thirty-one copies of the ordinary edition and one copy of the edition on *papier vélin*. In addition we found nine copies of a later edition, recognized by the text having been reset in twenty pages in folio (with vertical chain-lines). We have, however, a curious statement made by L'Héritier to J. E. Smith in his letter of 9 April 1792; "Cet ouvrage [*i.e.,* the *Sertum Anglicum*] a assez de debit. L'edition sur papier vélin est entierement epuisée, et il ne me reste que 60 à 80 exemplaires du papier ordinaire." (This work sells very well. The edition on wove paper is completely out of stock, and I have only 60 to 80 copies left of the ordinary paper [edition]). It is remarkable that so few copies have found their way to institutional libraries (we did not circularize private libraries). Dozens of copies alone were sent to England according to the invoices contained in the correspondence.

The later edition was also brought out by Didot. Since the twenty pages are set in such a way that the special texts for plates 1 and 2 no longer face them (the text is continuous), we must assume that this edition was put out at a time when Didot was certain that the text for the other plates would never be produced. This may have been during L'Héritier's lifetime but was more probably after his death. We have found no indication of the date of publication of this second edition, but for purposes of priority in botanical nomenclature this is unimportant. The text is unchanged (including that of the title-page) except for the omission of a few signs; the plates are evidently those of the original edition. It should be noted that two errors corrected by L'Héritier in his correspondence with Dryander (*disco* instead of *radio* on p. 27, last line but one, and *mox dilatatus* instead of *non dilatatus* on p. 11, sub no. 8) are *not* corrected in the 20-page edition. This makes it almost certain that L'Héritier had nothing to do with the reprinting of the text, and it is therefore highly probable that it was brought out after 1800. It can also be assumed that this edition was published as a whole and not in fascicles.

INSTITUTIONS POSSESSING SERTUM ANGLICUM

	Edition held		
	36-page edition		20-page edition
	Incomplete parts nos.:	Complete	
Amsterdam: University Library, Municipal University			×
Ann Arbor: University of Michigan	1		
Basel: Öffentliche Bibliothek der Universität		×	
Berkeley: University of California		× ×	
Bruxelles: Jardin botanique de l'Etat		×	
Cambridge (Mass.): Harvard University, Arnold Arboretum			×
Gray Herbarium		×	
Houghton Library		×	
Firenze: Istituto Botanico dell'Università		×	
Genève: Conservatoire botanique		×	
Haarlem: Teyler's Stichting		×	
Ithaca: Cornell University Library		×	
Jena: Institut für spezielle Botanik und Herbarium Haussknecht		×	
Kew: Royal Botanic Gardens		×	
Leiden: Rijksherbarium	1, 2		×
London: British Museum	1, 2 (2×)		
British Museum (Natural History)		×	
Linnean Society of London		×	
Royal Horticultural Soc., Lindley Library			×
Los Angeles: Allan Hancock Foundation Library		×	
New York: The New York Botanical Garden			×
Notre Dame: University of Notre Dame Library		×	
Oxford: Oxford University Bodleian Library	1		
Botany School	1		
Radcliffe Science Library		×	
Paris: Bibliothèque nationale		×	×
Muséum National d'Histoire naturelle, Laboratoire de Phanérogamie		×	
Philadelphia: Academy of Natural Sciences		×	
Pittsburgh: Hunt Botanical Library	1	×	
Renner, Texas: Texas Research Foundation			×
St. Louis: Missouri Botanical Garden			×
Stanford: Stanford University, Dudley Herbarium		×	
Stockholm: Royal Swedish Academy of Sciences	1	×	
Utrecht: Botanical Museum and Herbarium			×
Washington: National Agricultural Library		×	
The Dumbarton Oaks Research Library		×	
Wien: Österreichische Nationalbibliothek		×	

PREPARATION OF THE WORK

Dates in correspondence

20 Apr 1788: letter to Dryander, announcing *Sertum Anglicum*, *L'Héritier Corr.* 4.

8 Aug 1788: sends first three sheets to Dryander, *L'Héritier Corr.* 12.

21 Sep 1788: asks Dryander to send a motto, *L'Héritier Corr.* 19, and mentions the printing error "mox dilatatus" on page 11. This means that this part of the text had been printed already on that date.

2 Oct 1788: mentions to Dryander that he will ask Sowerby to make the 44th drawing *(Dicksonia)*, *L'Héritier Corr.* 21.

11 Dec 1788: asks Banks to announce the book in British reviews, *L'Héritier Corr.* 25.

SUMMARY OF DATES OF PUBLICATION

Fascicle 1, pages 1-36, plates i-ii: January 1789.

Fascicle 2, no text, plates iii-xii: May 1790.

Fascicle 3, no text, plates xiii-xxiv, xv bis: April 1792.

Fascicle 4, no text, plates xxv-xxxiv: late 1792.

These dates are based on contemporary reviews as well as on the correspondence between L'Héritier and his English friends.

FASCICLE I

Reviews

Obs. Phys. Hist. Nat. Arts 34: 79. Jan. 1789 (date of censor 28 Jan. 1789, review); 36: 24. Jan. 1790 (among list of books published in 1789).

Alg. Konst Letter-bode 2: 60. 20 Feb. 1789.

Gött. Gelehrte Anz. 1789: 116. 11 Jul. 1789.

Mag. Bot. Römer & Usteri 5: 184. 1789 sem. 2; 6: 58. 1789 sem. 2 (the book was received by the editors at the same time as the January 1789 issue of the *Obs. Phys. Hist. Nat. Arts*).

Monthly Rev. London 80: 640. Jun. 1789 ("a few sheets"); ser. 2. 1: 47. Jan. 1790 ("lately published").

Med.-chir. Zeit. Salzburg 1790 (2): 444. 24 Jun. 1790 (referred to as having been published in 1789).

Allg. Litt. Zeit. 1790 (4): 800. 27 Dec. 1790 (review of text and 12 plates, that is of fasc. 1 and 2).

Other dates:

20 Apr. 1788: date of preface.

11 Jun. 1789: received by Göttingen University Library (comm. W.T.Stearn).

Correspondence:

29 Dec. 1788 to Dryander: "I am adding to your copies of the *Sertum Anglicum* two copies for the Monthly and Critical Reviews", *L'Héritier Corr.* 27.

29 Jan. 1789: letter to Dryander answering him on a question regarding a printing error (p. 27 last line but one, last word must be *disco* instead of *radio*), *L'Héritier Corr.* 28.

FASCICLE 2

Reviews

Allg. Litt. Zeit. 1790 (4): 800. 27 Dec. 1790.

Gött. Gelehrte Anz. 1791: 343. 26 Feb. 1791.

Alg. Konst Letter-bode 6: 77. 11 Mar. 1791.

Ann. Bot. Usteri 1: 160. Sep.-Nov. 1791.

Other data:

8 Dec. 1790: received by Göttingen University Library (comm. W.T.Stearn).

Correspondence:

12 Feb. 1789: announces Dryander that fascicle 2 will appear in the course of 1789, *l'Héritier Corr.* 30.

24 May 1790: letter to J.E.Smith stating that part 2 is published, *Linn. Soc. Smith Mss.* 5, III.

1 Nov. 1790: asks Dryander whether he sent Banks a copy of fasc. 2 on wove paper or on ordinary paper, *L'Héritier Corr.* 47.

25 Dec. 1790: invoice for six copies in letter to J.E.Smith, *Linn. Soc. Smith Mss.* 5, 118.

25 Sep. 1791: invoice for another six copies in letter to J.E.Smith, *Linn. Soc. Smith Mss.* 5, 119.

FASCICLE 3

Reviews

Gött. Gelehrte Anz. 1792: 1695. 22 Oct. 1792.

Ann. Bot. Usteri 5: 109. 1793 prim. (mentions fascicle 3 as from 1792).

Correspondence:

9 Apr. 1792, letter to J.E.Smith containing an invoice for the sending of seven copies of the *Geraniologia,* and copies of fascicle 3, *Linn. Soc. Smith Mss.* 5, 121.

FASCICLE 4

Review

Ann. Bot. Usteri 5: 109. 1793 prim. (mentions fascicle 4 as from 1792).

From the letter to Dryander dated 29 December 1788 we may conclude that there is a possibility that the first fascicle was published in the last days of 1788. Since there is no further proof, and since several other sources quoted above point very clearly to publication in early January 1789, we think it better to adhere to this later date.

Since publication took place very early in 1789, the *Sertum Anglicum* has priority over practically all other 1789 publications, and, notwithstanding the title-page date, 1788, it can be assumed to have been published later than all 1788 publications.

REFERENCES

AITON, W. *Hortus Kewensis,* Vol. 1, p. xxi. London, 1789.

BARREIRO, A. J. Travels of Ruiz, Pavón, and Dombey in Peru and Chile (1777-1788). *Field Mus. Bot.* 21: 1-372. 1940.

BARTLETT, H. H. *Fifty-five rare books from the botanical library of Mrs. Roy Arthur Hunt,* p. 52. Ann Arbor, 1949.

BERTHOLLET, C.-L., C.-L. L'HÉRITIER ET P.-F. TISSOT. *Instruction sur la conservation et les usages des Pommes-de-terre,* publiée par la Commission d'Agriculture et des Arts. Paris, s.d. [1794-1795].

———— La Commission d'Agriculture et des Arts, aux autorités constituées. Deuxième instruction. *Extraction de l'Huile de Faine.* S.l., s.d. [Paris 1794-1795] (Two editions: one of 32 pp., one of 48 pp.).

————. *Rapport général sur les étangs,* fait au Comité d'Agriculture et des Arts, par la Commission d'Agriculture et des Arts. S.l., s.d. [Paris 1795].

BERTIN, L. ET AL. *Bvffon.* Paris, s.d. [1952].

BLUNT, W. *The art of botanical illustration,* pp. 159, 173, 174. London, 1950.

BOULGER, G. S. Dryander, Jonas. *Dict. Nat. Biogr.* 16: 64. 1888; [repr. 6: 64. 1921].

————. Smith, Sir James Edward. *Dict. Nat. Biogr.* 53: 61. 1898; [repr. 18: 469. 1922].

BRITTEN, J. AND G. S. BOULGER. *A biographical index of deceased British and Irish botanists.* Ed. 2, revised by A. B. Rendle. London, 1931.

BRITTEN, J. AND B. B. WOODWARD. Bibliographical notes, xxxv,—L'Héritier's botanical works. *Journ. Bot.* 43: 267-273, 325-329. 1905.

BRUNET, J.-C. *Manuel du libraire,* Ed. 5, vol. 3, p. 1043. Paris, s.d.

CANDOLLE, A. P. DE. Notice historique sur la vie et les travaux de M. Desfontaines. *Ann. Sc. Nat. Bot.* ser. 2, 1: 129-150. 1834.

———. *Mémoires et Souvenirs,* pp. 60, 62, 88, 94, 120. Genève, 1862.

CANDOLLE, ALPH. DE. *La phytographie,* p. 427. Paris, 1880.

CAP, P.-A. *Le Muséum d'Histoire naturelle,* pp. 45-46. Paris, 1854.

CAVANILLES, A. J. Observations... sur le cinquième fascicule de M. L'Héritier. *Obs. Phys. Hist. Nat. Arts* 34 (1): 183. 1789.

———. Observationes in quintum fasciculum D. L'Héritier. *Mag. Bot. Roemer et Usteri* 7: 42. 1790.

CUVIER, G. Notice historique sur Charles-Louis L'Héritier. *Mém. Inst. Nat. Sc. Arts, Cl. Sc. Math. Phys.* 4: 39-55. 1802.

DAVY DE VIRVILLE, A. *Histoire de la botanique en France,* pp. 61, 75, 80, 82, 85, 87, 115. Paris, 1954.

DAWSON, W. R. *Catalogue of the manuscripts in the library of the Linnean Society of London, Part I.—The Smith Papers.* London, 1934.

———. *The Banks letters.* London, 1958.

DEBURE, G. *Catalogue des livres de la bibliothèque de feu C. L. L'Héritier de Brutelle.* Paris, 1802 (Ed. 2, anon., 1805).

DÉHÉRAIN, H. Catalogue des manuscrits du fonds Cuvier. *Rev. Biblioth.* 1907: 30 (no. 180).

DELEUZE, J. P. F. Notice historique sur Joseph Dombey. *Ann. Mus. Hist. Nat.* 4: 136-169. 1804 (English translation *Ann. Bot. Konig et Sims* 2: 474-503. 1806).

DESHERBIERS, G. *Notice historique sur Charles-Louis L'Héritier,* Membre de l'Institut national, et de la Société libre des Lettres, Sciences et Arts de Paris; Lue à la Séance publique du 9 germinal an 9. Paris, 1801.

DRYANDER, J. *Catalogus bibliothecae historico-naturalis Josephi Banks.* 5 vols. London, 1798-1800.

DUBOIS, J.-B. Notice historique sur Malesherbes. *Mag. Enc.* 1795 (4): 355-414.

DUNTHORNE, G. *Flower and fruit prints of the 18th and early 19th centuries* p. 271. Washington, D. C., 1938.

GREDILLA, A. F. *Biografía de José Celestino Mutis,* pp. 129, 162, 690, 699. Madrid, 1911.

HAMY, E. T. *Joseph Dombey, médecin, naturaliste, ..., sa vie, son oeuvre, ...,* Paris, 1905.

HOEFER, (editor). Berthollet. *Nouv. Biogr. Gén.* 5: 716. 1855.

HOFMAN, N. [Letter to the Editor]. *Journ. Bot. Schrader* 1: 501. 1799.

JACKSON, B. D. Banks, Sir Joseph. *Dict. Nat. Biogr.* 3: 129. 1885; [repr. 1: 1049. 1921].

JACOB, ———. L'Héritier de Brutelle. *Nouv. Biogr. Gén.* 31: 70. 1860.

LACAZE, A. DE. Joseph Dombey. *Nouv. Biogr. Gén.* 14: 479. 1855.

LASÈGUE, A. *Musée botanique de M. Benjamin Delessert,* pp. 246, 345. Paris, 1845.

LEFEBVRE, G. *The French revolution from its origins to 1793.* London, 1962.

LÉGER, C. *Redouté et son temps,* pp. 12-14, 27-28, 151. Paris, 1945.

L'HÉRITIER, C.-L. *Stirpes novae.* Paris, 1784-1785 [publ. 1785-1791] (Six parts were published plus a conspectus of the contents of the seventh part; 184 pp. and plates 1-84. Plates bearing higher numbers or no numbers at all, found in some copies, stem from the August 1805 sale by DeBure and Merigot of the unpublished plates from L'Héritier's estate).

———. *Louichea,* S.l., s.d. [Dec. 1787].

———. *Virgilia,* S.l., s.d. [1788, sem. 1].

———. *Michauxia,* S.l., s.d. [1788, sem. 1].

———. *Buchozia,* S.l., s.d. [1788, sem. 2].

———. *Hymenopappus,* S.l. [1788, sem. 2].

———. Lettre ... à M. de la Métherie sur les Sidas, *Obs. Phys. Hist. Nat. Arts* 34 (1): 234. 1789.

———. *Cornus.* Paris, 1788 [publ. Jan.-Feb. 1789]. (Text reprinted in P. Usteri, *Del. opusc. bot.* vol. 2. 1793.)

———. On the genus of *Calligonum,* comprehending *Pterococcus* and *Pallasia. Trans. Linn. Soc.* 1: 177. 1791.

———. On the genus of *Symplocos,* comprehending *Hopea, Alstonia,* and *Ciponia. Trans. Linn. Soc.* 1: 174. 1791.

———. *Geraniologia.* Paris, 1787-88 [publ. Apr. 1792].

———. Mémoire sur un nouveau genre de plante appelé Cadia. *Mag. Enc.* 1795 (5): 20-31.

[*xli*]

L'Héritier, C.-L. Mémoire sur les effets du froid de ventôse an 4 (février et mars 1796) sur divers végétaux, et particulièrement sur le Poirier. *Mém. Inst. Nat. Sc. Arts* an 4, *Sc. Math. Phys.* 1: 169. 1798 [also in *Mag. Enc.* 1796 (6): 453-460].

———. See Berthollet, C.-L.

Louisy, P. Malesherbes. *Nouv. Biogr. Gén.* 33: 22. 1860.

Métherie, M. de la. Discours préliminaire. *Obs. Phys. Hist. Nat. Arts* 34 (1): 1. 1789.

M-R-L, J. Tissot. *Nouv. Biogr. Gén.* 45: 430. 1866.

Nissen, C. *Die botanische Buchillustration* vol. 1, pp. 138-142; vol. 2, pp. 108-109. Stuttgart, 1951.

Pritzel, G. A. *Thesaurus literaturae botanicae*, p. 156. Leipzig, 1851: Ed. 2, p. 184, Leipzig, 1872.

Redouté, P.-J. *Les Roses*, vol. 3, p. 22. Paris, 1817.

Reynolds Green, J. *A history of botany in the United Kingdom,* pp. 268, 270, 281. London, 1914.

Rickett, H. W. et F. A. Stafleu. Nomina generica conservanda et rejicienda spermatophytorum VIII, Bibliographia. *Taxon* 10: 113. 1961.

Smith, J. E. *A sketch of a tour on the continent in the years 1786 and 1787,* vol. 1; pp. 68, 124. London, 1793.

———. Dombey. *Rees Cyclopedia* 12: [no pagination]. 1809.

———. Héritier. *Rees Cyclopedia* 17: [no pagination]. 1811.

———. *Memoir and Correspondence* vol. 1, p. 331. London, 1832.

Stearn, W. T. Botanical gardens and botanical literature in the eighteenth century. *Catalogue of botanical books in the collection of Rachel McMasters Miller Hunt* vol. 2 (1), pp. cv-cvi. Pittsburgh, 1961.

Steenis-Kruseman, M. J. van. Dates of Publication. *Flora Malesiana* 4 (5): cxcvii, 1954.

Stevenson, A. *Catalogue of botanical books in the collection of Rachel McMasters Miller Hunt* vol. 2 (2), p. 468. Pittsburgh, 1961.

W———, S. L'Héritier de Brutelle, Charles-Louis, *Biogr. Univ. (Michaud)* 24: 442-443. s.d.

OTHER SOURCES

Académie des Sciences, Institut de France, Paris, France.

Letters from L'Héritier to Silvestre de Sacy (20 thermidor, an 7) and A. L. de Jussieu (15 June 1789).

Note written by L'Héritier on plants asked from Ortega (23 March 1782).

Letter from [Charles] L'Héritier to the Institut de France. s.d. (translation body).

Court judgment on heritage (5 brumaire, an 9) (extract).

Letter signed by de St. Priest and de Condorcet announcing the appointment of L'Héritier as associate member of the *Académie des Sciences* (17 May 1790).

Index biographique des membres et correspondants de l'Académie des Sciences du 22 décembre 1666 au 15 novembre 1954. — Paris 1954.

Procès-verbaux des séances de l'Académie tenues depuis la fondation de l'Institut jusqu'au mois d'août 1835 — vol. 1 (ans 4-8) (1796-1799) Hendaye 1910, vol. 2 (ans 8-11) (1800-1804) Hendaye 1912.

Archives nationales, Paris, France.

Police reports on the death of L'Héritier: 29 thermidor and 7 fructidor an 8 (Préfecture de police, carton F 7, no. 3844). These reports fix the murder at 28 thermidor, against 23.00 hours.

Notary act in "Minutier des notaires", made by Notary Mesnard 8 fructidor an 8.

Documents concerning the Muséum national d'Histoire naturelle File AJ 15-584. Reports on the meetings of the administrative professors of the Museum of 4, 14 and 24 fructidor, an 8; a letter to the government on the L'Héritier library (16 fructidor); letter to L'Héritier heirs on Dombey herbaria and manuscripts (17 fructidor); letter Marie L'Héritier to Thouin on same (21 fructidor).

Archives de la Seine et de la Ville de Paris, Paris, France.

Acte de décès de Charles Louis L'Héritier, 29 thermidor an 8.

Déclaration de succession, 23 nivose an 9 (Document DQ 7, 1766, fo. 181 vo).

Bibliothèque nationale, Paris, France.

    Journal des débats et loix du pouvoir législatif et des actes du gouvernement, Paris, 30 thermidor, an 8 (report on murder, committed on 28 thermidor, late at night).

    Gazette nationale ou le Moniteur universel, no. 331, 1 fructidor, an 8, pp. 1334-1335. (Report on murder.)

Bibliothèque centrale, Muséum national d'Histoire naturelle, Paris, France.

    Letters from L'Héritier to Deleuze (6 May 1794) and La Peyrouse (8 July 1786, 13 October 1796, 2 November 1796, 7 December 1799).

    Kakile, cum animadversionibus in Buniadem, Myagrum et Crambem. 1788. [Paris, proofsheets, unpublished memoir signed Car. Lud. L'Héritier.]

Laboratoire de Phanérogamie, Muséum national d'Histoire naturelle, Paris, France.

    Letters L'Héritier to Mme. L'Héritier s.d., to A. L. de Jussieu (2 June 1789).

    Mémoire sur un nouveau genre de plants appelé Redoutea par Ch. Louis L'Héritier (unpublished manuscript).

    Cavanilles correspondence, a collection of forty-eight letters written by A. J. Cavanilles to A. L. de Jussieu.

Biohistorisch Instituut van de Rijksuniversiteit, Utrecht, Netherlands.

    Index Botanicorum, a file of references to biographical data.

    Letter L'Héritier to Pourret (2 September 1782).

Conservatoire et Jardin botaniques, Genève, Switzerland.

    L'Héritier de Brutelle, Manuscripta botanica, four boxes.

    Letter from L'Héritier to M. Vahl (23 January 1784).

    Compendium geraniologium, manuscript and four proof-sheets, "Parisiis 1789", not published.

Botany Department, British Museum (Natural History), London, Great Britain.

    L'Héritier correspondence — A series of fifty-one autograph letters by L'Héritier, mainly to J. Dryander and J. Banks, quoted by serial numbers. Department of Botany, British Museum (Natural History).

    Dryander correspondence — Correspondence of J. Dryander in the Department of Botany, British Museum (Natural History). Quoted by serial numbers (consulted nos. 10-13).

    Dawson Turner copies of the correspondence of Joseph Banks, vol. 5 nos. 60-62, 83-88, 93-97, 263 and vol. 6 nos. 25-25, 31-32.

British Museum (Bloomsbury), London, Great Britain.

    Banks correspondence — W. R. Dawson, 1958, gives "a calendar of the manuscript correspondence of Joseph Banks preserved in the British Museum, the British Museum (Natural History) and other collections in Great Britain." (From Additional Manuscripts, volumes 8095, 8096, 8099, 33272, and 33982). [By means of this excellent work all letters received by Banks and mentioned in this introduction can easily be traced.]

The Linnean Society of London, London, Great Britain.

    The Smith Papers. Dawson, 1934, provides a catalogue of the correspondence and miscellaneous papers of J. E. Smith. Consulted vol. 1 nos. 81-84 and vol. 5 nos. 81-127, 223-234 (cited as *Linn. Soc., Smith Mss.*).

The plants of Sertum Anglicum

J. S. L. Gilmour, C. J. King, and L. H. J. Williams

The origin, scope, and publication of L'Héritier's tribute to the country in which he spent fifteen such fruitful months during 1786 and 1787 have been described in detail in the foregoing essay. As the title-page of the *Sertum* indicates, many of the plants included by L'Héritier were growing at the time in British gardens, but in fact he drew on much wider and more varied sources to collect together the 125 species he described. In his new genus *Prismatocarpus,* for example, under which he included nine species, only two (*P. fruticosus* and *P. nitidus*) were, according to Aiton's *Hortus Kewensis* (1789), cultivated at Kew at that time (both recently introduced by Francis Masson); four others (*P. interruptus, P. paniculatus, P. altiflorus,* and *P. crispus*) were described from specimens in Banks's herbarium, collected at the Cape (South Africa) by Thunberg, Augé, Masson, and Augé respectively; while the remaining three (*P. Speculum, P. hybridus,* and *P. Pentagonia*) were well-known Linnaean species of *Campanula* transferred by L'Héritier to his new genus. [Here, and elsewhere in this essay, L'Héritier's names are used for the reader's ease in reference, regardless of their correctness. Ed.]

An examination of the text, and of available manuscripts, relating to the full range of species included in the *Sertum* enables a classification to be drawn up into the following nine groups, based on the source of the material used by L'Héritier for his descriptions and illustrations.

1. Plants seen alive at Kew or other British gardens; in some cases herbarium material may also have been seen, but not necessarily so. The following are a few selected examples of species in this category. Kew: *Roëlla decurrens, Tradescantia discolor,* and *Relhania squarrosa.* James Lee's nursery at Hammersmith: *Chloranthus inconspicuus* (also at Kew). The Duke of Northumberland's garden at Syon House: *Hamelia grandiflora.* James Vere's garden at Kensington: *Mimosa grandiflora.* Lord Petre's garden: *Witheringia solanacea.*

2. Plants seen alive at Kew (and sometimes in other British gardens) and also as dried specimens in Banks's herbarium. This class includes many of the plants collected by Francis Masson (*e.g., Lightfootia oxycoccoides, Rhamnus latifolius,* and *Cineraria cruenta*) and by other collectors who brought back both living and dried plants (*e.g., Tamus elephantipes,* collected by Nelson at the Cape, and *Dicksonia arborescens,* herbarium specimens of which were collected by Banks on St. Helena, and which was introduced to Kew as a living plant in 1786 by Anthony Hove).

3. Plants seen in Banks's herbarium only and not, as far as can be traced, as living specimens, at Kew or elsewhere. The following are a few selected examples: L'Héritier's new species of *Relhania; Eucalyptus obliqua* (immature plants were probably at Kew, but

the description and plate are based on herbarium specimens collected by Nelson and Anderson); *Amaryllis clavata* (L'Héritier states in a letter to Dryander that he based his description on the dried specimen from Kew in Banks's herbarium); *Dicksonia Culcita* (though this was growing at Kew, L'Héritier states in a letter to Dryander that he had not seen it).

4. Plants described from living material seen in the Paris garden. Examples are: *Rhamnus hybridus, Rhamnus alnifolius* (also seen in James Lee's nursery at Hammersmith, according to a letter to Dryander), *Celastrus phyllacanthus* (introduced by Adanson), and *Celastrus octagonus* (grown from seed collected by Dombey; also grown at Kew from seed collected by Thouin).

5. Plants described from specimens in Dombey's herbarium. Only the following five species were included in the *Sertum*—rather a meagre harvest after all the trouble that L'Héritier took to get possession of the herbarium: *Amaryllis tubiflora, A. maculata, A. chilensis, Bystropogon pectinatum,* and *B. sidaefolium.*

6. Plants described from specimens in herbaria other than those of Banks and Dombey. These include *Amaryllis tubispatha* (collected by Commerson in Buenos Aires, specimen now at Geneva), *Stokesia cyanea* (seen at Kew, but described from a specimen collected by Gordon, now at Geneva), and *Mimosa Houstoni* (specimen from Miller's herbarium, now at Geneva).

7. Descriptions based on drawings by Bruguière. These include only two species, *Amaryllis spiralis* and *A. cinnamomea.* Both drawings were sent by L'Héritier to Dryander and are now at the British Museum (Natural History).

8. Description based on a drawing in Banks's library. *Amaryllis revoluta* is the only species in this category.

9. Plants already described by previous authors, but included by L'Héritier in the *Sertum,* sometimes under a new genus. Specimens of many of these were, of course, seen by L'Héritier in gardens or in herbaria. Examples of generic changes are Linnaeus's three species of *Campanula,* mentioned above, placed by L'Héritier in his new genus *Prismatocarpus,* and Linnaeus's *Crinum latifolium* transferred by L'Héritier to *Amaryllis.* In many cases, of course, L'Héritier did not adopt the original epithet when he transferred a plant to a different genus, but proposed a new one (a practice then current, but now regarded as illegitimate) which he no doubt considered more appropriate; for example, he transferred Linnaeus's *Crinum obliquum* to *Amaryllis* under the name *A. Umbella.* The oriental goldenrain-tree, *Koelreuteria paniculata* Laxmann, he renamed *K. paullinioides* without change of genus.

One point of interest that emerges from this survey of the sources tapped by L'Héritier for his *Sertum* is that nearly all the species that were illustrated (or intended for illustration) had been seen as living specimens by L'Héritier at Kew or elsewhere. He evidently fully appreciated the suitability of living, as opposed to dried, specimens as subjects for a botanical artist.

Despite the fact that many of the species included in the *Sertum* were described from herbarium specimens, many, as we have seen, were examined by L'Héritier as live specimens growing at Kew and other British gardens, and the present-day reader is struck very forcibly by the wide range of genera and species cultivated in Britain at that time—many having since been lost to cultivation.

It was, of course, the period of the great plant collectors, and the journeys of Masson, Nelson, Thunberg, Solander, Banks himself, and many others resulted in a steady stream of new species flowing into British gardens. [For a list of plant collectors cited in the *Sertum* see that given at the end of this essay. Ed.] Many of these species were of purely botanical, rather than horticultural, interest, and the *Sertum* does not, in fact, include a great many plants which are familiar to present-day gardeners in Britain. Of the thirteen new genera described by L'Héritier (*Witheringia, Prismatocarpus, Lightfootia, Pitcairnia, Agapanthus, Eucomis, Eucalyptus, Bystropogon, Relhania, Boltonia, Stokesia, Genesiphylla,* and *Dicksonia*), only *Agapanthus, Eucomis, Eucalyptus,* and possibly *Dicksonia*, can now be regarded as important horticultural genera in Britain. Under *Dicksonia* L'Héritier named for the first time, as *D. Culcita,* the "Cushion Fern" from Madeira and the Azores (*Culcita macrocarpa* Presl), though, as shown by his footnote, he was very doubtful whether it should be regarded as distinct from the famous Tartarian or Vegetable Lamb (*Cibotium barometz* (L.) J. Sm.) from the Far East, to which there is a long list of literature references in the L'Héritier manuscript at Geneva. The specimen he described, now at the British Museum, had been collected by Masson on the island of St. Miguel, in the Azores, and L'Héritier records that the inhabitants make mattresses ("Culcitas") from its roots (*i.e.,* from the abundant soft, silky hairs on the crown and bases of its fronds).

Under already established genera, L'Héritier described for the first time the following species of horticultural interest:- *Tradescantia discolor* (=*Rhoeo spathacea* (Swartz) Stearn, Syn. *R. discolor* (L'Hérit.) Hance), *Tamus elephantipes* (=*Testudinaria elephantipes* (L'Hérit.) Salisb.), *Mimosa verticillata* (=*Acacia verticillata* (L'Hérit.) Willd.), and *Cineraria cruenta* (=*Senecio cruentus* (L'Hérit.) DC.), the main, and perhaps the only, species from which the modern greenhouse Cinerarias have been derived. Other present-day garden plants which he included, but was not the first to describe, were several under *Amaryllis,* including *A. lutea* (=*Sternbergia lutea* (L.) Spreng.), and *A. belladonna* L. (Syn. *Brunsvigia rosea* (Lam.) Hannibal), and *Koelreuteria paniculata* Laxm. (under the illegitimate name *K. paullinioides*). Thus L'Héritier's work, as one would expect, is primarily that of a botanist, though the garden plants he included make it also of considerable interest to horticulturalists who are concerned with the early history of the plants they grow.

The following list consists of the genera and species included in the *Sertum,* arranged in L'Héritier's order. Under each genus the place of publication, the type species, and the family name are given. The species are listed under the names used by L'Héritier, followed by the page and plate reference in the *Sertum,* an indication in square brackets if the plant was described as a new species or if the name was an illegitimate one, and the modern name or names of the plant concerned. These modern names are not based on original taxonomic or nomenclatural research, but are taken from standard works and are intended to lead readers to present-day literature on L'Héritier's plants. Following the modern names, the geographical distribution of the species is given in broad terms. Mention is then made of herbarium specimens (type (original) specimen, or otherwise) which were presumably seen by L'Héritier, and are now at the British

Museum (Natural History) London, at Paris, or at Geneva, followed by an indication ("Mss. at G") of those cases where there is a manuscript description of the species concerned in the L'Héritier papers at Geneva. These descriptions at Geneva may be regarded as rough preliminary drafts for the more detailed texts that L'Héritier planned but never published, and contain much information of importance, both taxonomic and as regards provenance. Finally, particulars are given, where known, of the introduction of the species into Britain.

GENERA AND SPECIES INCLUDED IN SERTUM ANGLICUM

WITHERINGIA L'Hérit., Sert. Angl. 1, 33. 1788 [1789]. Solanaceae. T.: *W. solanacea* L'Hérit.

> WITHERINGIA SOLANACEA (pp. 1 & 33, t. 1) [sp. nov.] = **Capsicum solanaceum** (L'Hérit.) O.Ktze. (*Bàssovia solanacea* (L'Hérit.) Benth. & Hook. f.)—S. America. Specimen (? type: Hort. Kew, 1777) in BM. [Mss. at G] Introduction: before 1742 (Aiton, Hort. Kew., 1789).

CHLORANTHUS Sw., Philos. Trans. Roy. Soc. 77: 359. 1787. Chloranthaceae. T.: *C. inconspicuus* Sw.

> CHLORANTHUS INCONSPICUUS (pp. 1 & 35, t. 2) = **C. spicatus** (Thunb.) Mak. (*C. inconspicuus* Sw.).—China. Specimen in BM. Introduction: 1781 by J. Lind (Aiton, Hort. Kew., 1789).

PRISMATOCARPUS L'Hérit., Sert. Angl. 1. 1788 [1789]. Campanulaceae. T.: *Campanula speculum-veneris* L. *Prismatocarpus* is a superfluous name for *Legousia* Durande, and its type is automatically that of *Legousia*.

> PRISMATOCARPUS INTERRUPTUS (p. 2) [sp. nov.] = **P. pedunculatus** (Berg.) A. DC. (*fide* Adamson in Journ. S. Afr. Bot. 17: 98. 1951).—South Africa. Specimen (type: Thunberg, Cape of Good Hope) in BM. Introduction: 1818 (Loudon, Hort. Brit., 1830).

> PRISMATOCARPUS PANICULATUS (p. 2) [sp. nov.] = **P. pedunculatus** (Berg.) A. DC. (*fide* Adamson in Journ. S. Afr. Bot. 17: 97. 1951).—South Africa. Specimen (type: Augé, S. Africa) in BM. Introduction: 1818 (Loudon, Hort. Brit., 1830).

> PRISMATOCARPUS ALTIFLORUS (p. 2) [sp. nov.] = **P. altiflorus** L'Hérit.—South Africa. Specimen (type, Masson, Cape of Good Hope) in BM.

> PRISMATOCARPUS FRUTICOSUS (p. 2) = **P. fruticosus** (L.) L'Hérit. (*P. subulatus* (Thunb.) A. DC.). —South Africa. Specimen (type: Masson, Cape of Good Hope) in BM. Introduction: 1787 by F. Masson (Aiton, Hort. Kew., 1789, sub *Campanula fruticosa*).

> PRISMATOCARPUS CRISPUS (p. 2) [sp. nov.] = **P. crispus** L'Hérit.—South Africa. Specimen (type: Augé, Cape of Good Hope) in BM.

> PRISMATOCARPUS NITIDUS (p. 2, t. 3) [sp. nov.] = **P. nitidus** L'Hérit.—South Africa. Specimen (type: Masson, Cape of Good Hope) in BM. Introduction: 1787 (Aiton, Hort. Kew., 1789, sub *Campanula prismatocarpus*).

> PRISMATOCARPUS SPECULUM (p. 3) = **Legousia speculum-veneris** (L.) Chaix.—C. Europe and Mediterranean region. Specimens in BM. Introduction: 1596 (Loudon, Hort. Brit., 1830).

PRISMATOCARPUS HYBRIDUS (p. 3) = **Legousia hybrida** (L.) Delarb.—Europe, W. Asia, N. Africa. Specimen in BM.

PRISMATOCARPUS PENTAGONIA (p. 3) = **Legousia pentagonia** (L.) Thell.—W. Asia and E. Mediterranean.

LIGHTFOOTIA L'Hérit., Sert. Angl. 4. 1788 [1789]. Campanulaceae. LT.: *L. oxycoccoides* L'Hérit.

LIGHTFOOTIA OXYCOCCOIDES (p. 4, t. 4) [*nom. illegit.*] = **L. parvifolia** (Berg.) Adamson (*fide* Adamson, Journ. S. Afr. Bot. 21: 166. 1955).—South Africa. Specimen (type: Masson, Cape of Good Hope) in BM. Introduction: 1787 by F. Masson (Aiton, Hort. Kew., 1789).

LIGHTFOOTIA SUBULATA (p. 4, t. 5) [sp. nov.] = **L. subulata** L'Hérit. (*L. sessiliflora* (L.f.) Sond. non Spreng., *fide* Adamson in Journ. S. Afr. Bot. 19: 157. 1953). —South Africa. Specimens (type: Masson and Nelson, Cape of Good Hope) in BM. Introduction: 1787 (Aiton, Hort. Kew., 1789).

ROËLLA L., Sp. Pl. 170. 1753. Campanulaceae. LT.: *R. ciliata* L.

ROËLLA DECURRENS (p. 4, t. 6) [sp. nov.] = **R. decurrens** L'Hérit. *fide* Adamson and Salter, Fl. Cape Penin. 744. 1950. (= *Wahlenbergia capensis* (L.) A. DC. *fide* W. T. Stearn, R. H. S. Dict. Gard.. 1951).—South Africa. Specimen (Hort. Kew, not Masson) in BM. Introduction: 1787 (Aiton, Hort. Kew. 1789).

HAMELIA Jacq., Enum. Pl. Carib. 2, 16. 1760. Rubiaceae LT.: *H. patens* Jacq.

HAMELIA PATENS L. (p. 4) = **H. patens** Jacq.—Tropical America and West Indies. Introduction: 1752 (R. H. S. Dict. Gard., 1951).

HAMELIA GRANDIFLORA (p. 4, t. 7) [sp. nov.] = **H. ventricosa** Sw.—West Indies. Specimen (type: Shakespear, Wright, and Swartz, Jamaica) in BM. [Mss at G] Introduction: 1778 by T. Clark (Aiton, Hort. Kew., 1789).

RHAMNUS L., Sp. Pl. 193. 1753. Rhamnaceae. LT.: *R. catharticus* L.

RHAMNUS HYBRIDUS (p. 5) [hybrid. nov.] = **R. × hybrida** L'Hérit. (*R. alaternus × alpinus*).—Only in cultivation. Specimen (? type: Hort. Reg. Paris) in G.

RHAMNUS ALNIFOLIUS (p. 5) [sp. nov.] = **R. alnifolia** L'Hérit.—N. America. Specimen (? type: Michaux, N. America) in P. Introduction: 1778 by Messrs Lee and Kennedy (Aiton, Hort. Kew., 1789).

RHAMNUS VOLUBILIS L. (p. 5) = **Berchemia scandens** (J. Hill) K. Koch.—S. United States. Introduction: before 1714 (Aiton, Hort. Kew., 1789).

RHAMNUS LATIFOLIUS (p. 5, t. 8) [sp. nov.] = **R. latifolia** L'Hérit. —Azores. Specimen (type: Masson, Azores) in BM. [Mss. at G] Introduction: 1778 (Aiton, Hort. Kew., 1789).

RHAMNUS PRINOIDES (p. 6, t. 9) [sp. nov.] = **R. prinoides** L'Hérit. —South Africa. Specimens (type: Augé and Masson on one sheet) in G. [Mss. at G] Introduction: before 1779 (Aiton, Hort. Kew., 1789).

RHAMNUS MICRANTHUS L. (p. 6) = **Trema micrantha** (L.) Blume.—Tropical America and West Indies.

CEANOTHUS L., Sp. Pl. 195. 1753. Rhamnaceae. LT.: *C. americanus* L.

CEANOTHUS RECLINATUS (p. 6) [sp. nov.] = **Colubrina reclinata** (L'Hérit.) Brongn.—C. America and West Indies.

CELASTRUS L., Sp. Pl. 196. 1753. Celastraceae. LT.: *C. scandens* L.

CELASTRUS CORNICULATUS (p. 6) (= *Euclea racemosa* L'Hérit. Sertum, 32, non L.) = **Kiggelaria dregeana** Turcz. var. **obtusa** Harv. (Flacourtiaceae) (*fide* Hiern in Harvey & Sonder, Fl. Cap. 4 (1): 474. 1909). [Mss. at G]—South Africa.

CELASTRUS CASSINOIDES (p. 6, t. 10) [sp. nov.] = **Gymnosporia cassinoides** (L'Hérit.) Masf.— Canary Islands. Specimen (type: Masson, Tenerife) in BM. [Mss. at G] Introduction: 1779 (Aiton, Hort. Kew., 1789).

CELASTRUS PHYLLACANTHUS (p. 6) [sp. nov.] = **Maytenus senegalensis** (Lam.) Exell.—Old World tropics and subtropics. Introduction: to Paris before 1788.

CELASTRUS OCTOGONUS (p. 7) = **Maytenus octogona** (L'Hérit.) DC. —S. America. Introduction: 1786 by Thouin (Aiton, Hort. Kew., 1789).

CELASTRUS UNDULATUS (p. 7) [sp. nov.] = **Pittosporum senacia** Putterl.—Mauritius and Seychelles. Introduction: 1785 by Messrs Lee and Kennedy (Aiton, Hort. Kew., 1789).

PITCAIRNIA L'Hérit., Sert. Angl. 7. 1788 [1789]. Bromeliaceae. T.: *P. bromeliaefolia* L'Hérit.

PITCAIRNIA BROMELIAEFOLIA (p..7, t. 11) [sp. nov.] = **P. bromeliifolia** L'Hérit.—West Indies. Introduction: before 1781 (Aiton, Hort. Kew., 1789).

TRADESCANTIA L., Sp. Pl. 288. 1753. Commelinaceae. T.: *T. virginiana* L.

TRADESCANTIA DISCOLOR (p. 8, t. 12) [sp. nov.] = **Rhoeo spathacea** (Swartz) Stearn, *conf.* Stearn in Baileya 5: 195-198. 1957. (*R. discolor* (L'Hérit.) Hance.)—C. America and West Indies. Introduction: 1783 by M. Wallen (Aiton, Hort. Kew., 1789).

CRINUM L., Sp. Pl. 291. 1753. Amaryllidaceae. LT.: *C. americanum* L.

CRINUM ASIATICUM L. (p. 8) = **C. asiaticum** L.—Tropical Asia. Specimens in BM. Introduction: 1732 (Loudon, Hort. Brit., 1830).

CRINUM AMERICANUM L. (p. 8) = **C. americanum** L.—S. United States. Introduction: before 1732 (Aiton, Hort. Kew., 1789).

CRINUM NERVOSUM (p. 8) [sp. nov.] = **Eurycles amboinensis** (L.) Loud. (*E. sylvestris* Salisb.).— Malaya, Philippines, Australia. Introduction: 1759 (R. H. S. Dict. Gard., 1951).

AMARYLLIS L., Sp. Pl. 292. 1753. Amaryllidaceae. [Mss. at G, including synopsis and notes on several species.] LT.: *A. belladonna* L.

AMARYLLIS LUTEA L. (p. 9) = **Sternbergia lutea** (L.) Spreng.—Mediterranean region and W. Asia. Introduction: before 1596 (Aiton, Hort. Kew., 1789).

AMARYLLIS TUBISPATHA (p. 9) [sp. nov.] = **Zephyranthes tubispatha** (L'Hérit.) Herb.—West Indies and S. America. Specimen (type: Commerson, Buenos Aires) in G.

AMARYLLIS TUBIFLORA (p. 10) [sp. nov.] = **Zephyranthes tubiflora** (L'Hérit.) Schinz (*Z. aurea* (Ruiz & Pav.) Baker).—Peru. Specimen (type: Dombey, Lima) in BM.

AMARYLLIS SPIRALIS (p. 10, t. 13) [sp. nov.] = **Carpolyza tenella** (L.f.) Leighton (*fide* Adamson and Salter, Fl. Cape Penin. 213. 1950).—South Africa. Specimens in BM. Introduction: 1774 by F. Masson (Aiton, Hort. Kew., 1789, sub *Haemanthus spiralis*).

AMARYLLIS ATAMASCO L. (p. 10) = **Zephyranthes atamasco** (L.) Herb.—S. E. United States. Specimen in BM. Introduction: before 1680 (Aiton, Hort. Kew., 1789).

AMARYLLIS MACULATA (p. 10) [sp. nov.] = **Habranthus maculatus** (L'Hérit.) Herb.—S. America. Specimen (type: Dombey, Chile) in P.

AMARYLLIS CHILENSIS (p. 11) [sp. nov.] = **Rhodophiala chilensis** (L'Hérit.) Traub. (*Hippeastrum chilense* (L'Hérit.) Baker).—S. America. Specimen (type: Dombey, Chile) in P.

AMARYLLIS CLAVATA (p. 11) [sp. nov.] = **Cyrtanthus clavatus** (L'Hérit.) R. A. Dyer.—South Africa. Specimen (? type: Hort. Kew) in BM. Introduction: 1816 (R. H. S. Dict. Gard., 1951).

AMARYLLIS FORMOSISSIMA L. (p. 11) = **Sprekelia formosissima** (L.) Herb.—C. America. Introduction: before 1658 (Aiton, Hort. Kew., 1789).

AMARYLIS REGINAE (p. 11) = **Hippeastrum reginae** (L.) Herb. (*A. reginae* L.).—West Indies and S. America. Introduction: before 1725 (Aiton, Hort. Kew., 1789).

AMARYLLIS SPECIOSA (p. 12) = **Vallota speciosa** (L.f.) Durand & Schinz.—South Africa. Specimen in BM. Introduction: 1774 (Aiton, Hort. Kew., 1789, sub *A. purpurea*).

AMARYLLIS BELLADONNA (p. 12) = **A. belladonna** L. (*Brunsvigia rosea* (Lam.) Hannibal).—South Africa. Introduction: about 1712 (Aiton, Hort. Kew., 1789).

AMARYLLIS RETICULATA (p. 12, t. 14) [sp. nov.] = **Hippeastrum reticulatum** (L'Hérit.) Herb.—Brazil. Specimen (? type: de Ponthieu, West Indies) in BM. Introduction: 1777 by E. W. Gray (Aiton, Hort. Kew., 1789).

AMARYLLIS VITTATA (p. 13, t. 15) [sp. nov.] = **Hippeastrum vittatum** (L'Hérit.) Herb.—Peru and Brazil. Specimens (type: Hort. Malcolm) in BM. Introduction: 1769 by W. Malcolm (Aiton, Hort. Kew., 1789).

AMARYLLIS FALCATA (p. 13) = **Cybistetes longifolia** (L.) Milne-Redh. & Schweick.—South Africa. Introduction: 1773 by F. Masson (Aiton, Hort. Kew., 1789, sub *A. longifolia*).

AMARYLLIS LONGIFOLIA L. (p. 13) = **Cybistetes longifolia** (L.) Milne-Redh. & Schweick.—South Africa. Introduction: 1773 by F. Masson (Aiton, Hort. Kew., 1789).

AMARYLLIS ZEYLANICA L. (p. 13) = **Crinum zeylanicum** L.—Tropical Asia and Africa. Introduction: 1771 (R. H. S. Dict. Gard., 1951).

AMARYLLIS REVOLUTA (p. 14) [sp. nov.] = **Crinum lineare** L.f.—South Africa. Introduction: 1774 (Aiton, Hort. Kew., 1789).

AMARYLLIS LATIFOLIA (p. 14) = **Crinum latifolium** L.—Tropical Asia. Introduction: 1806 (R. H. S. Dict. Gard., 1951).

AMARYLLIS AUREA (p. 14, t. 15 *bis*) [sp. nov.] = **Lycoris aurea** (L'Hérit.) Herb.—China. Specimens (? type) in BM. Introduction: 1777 by J. Fothergill (Aiton, Hort. Kew., 1789).

AMARYLLIS ORIENTALIS L. (p. 14) = **Brunsvigia orientalis** (L.) Ait. ex Eckl. (*B. gigantea* Heist.).—South Africa. Introduction: 1767 by W. Malcolm (Aiton, Hort. Kew., 1789).

AMARYLLIS CILIARIS L. (p. 15) = **Boophone ciliaris** (L.) Herb. (*B. guttata* (L.) Herb., *fide* Adamson and Salter, Fl. Cape Penin. 210. 1950).—South Africa. Introduction: 1774 by F. Masson (Aiton, Hort. Kew., 1789, sub *Haemanthus ciliaris*).

AMARYLLIS UMBELLA (p. 15, t. 16) [*nom. illegit.*] = **Cyrtanthus obliquus** (L.f.) Ait.—South Africa. Specimen in BM. Introduction: 1774 (Aiton, Hort. Kew., 1789).

AMARYLLIS CYLINDRACEA (p. 15) [*nom. illegit.*] = **Cyrtanthus angustifolius** (L.f.) Ait.—South Africa. Specimens in BM. Introduction: 1774 (Aiton, Hort. Kew., 1789).

AMARYLLIS SARNIENSIS L. (p. 15) = **Nerine sarniensis** (L.) Herb.—South Africa. Specimens in BM. Introduction: 1659 (Loudon, Hort. Brit., 1830).

AMARYLLIS RADIATA (p. 16) [sp. nov.] = **Lycoris radiata** (L'Hérit.) Herb.—China and Japan. Specimens (type: Hort. Lee) in BM. Introduction: 1750 (Bot. Reg., t. 596. 1821).

AMARYLLIS CINNAMOMEA (p. 16, t. 17) [sp. nov.] = **Periphanes cinnamomea** (L'Hérit.) Leighton (*Hessea crispa* Kunth).—South Africa. Specimen (? type: Cape of Good Hope) in P.

AMARYLLIS UNDULATA L. (p. 16) = **Nerine undulata** (L.) Herb.—South Africa. Specimen in BM. Introduction: about 1767 by J. Blackburne (Aiton, Hort. Kew., 1789).

AGAPANTHUS L'Hérit., Sert. Angl. 17. 1788 [1789]. Liliaceae. T.: *A. umbellatus* L'Hérit. [*nom. illegit.*] = *Crinum africanum* L., *A. africanus* (L.) Hoffmgg.

AGAPANTHUS UMBELLATUS (p. 17) [*nom. illegit.*] = **A. africanus** (L.) Hoffmgg.—South Africa. Specimen in BM. Introduction: 1629 (R. H. S. Dict. Gard. Suppl., 1956).

EUCOMIS L'Hérit., Sert. Angl. 17. 1788 [1789]. Liliaceae. LT.: *E. regia* (L.) L'Hérit. (*Fritillaria regia* L.)

EUCOMIS REGIA (p. 17) = **E. regia** (L.) L'Hérit.—South Africa. Specimens in BM. Introduction: cultivated by the Duchess of Beaufort in 1709 (Aiton, Hort. Kew., 1789).

EUCOMIS NANA (p. 17) = **E. nana** (Burm.f.) L'Hérit.—South Africa. Specimen in BM. Introduction: 1774 by F. Masson (Aiton, Hort, Kew., 1789).

EUCOMIS PUNCTATA (p. 18, t. 18) [sp. nov.] = **E. punctata** L'Hérit.—South Africa. Specimen (?type: Hort.) in BM. [Mss. at G] Introduction: 1783 by J. Graefer (Aiton, Hort. Kew., 1789).

KOELREUTERIA Laxm., Novi Comm. Acad. Sc. Petropol. 16: 562. 1772. Sapindaceae. T.: *K. paniculata* Laxm.

KOELREUTERIA PAULLINIOIDES (p. 18, t. 19) [*nom. illegit.*] = **K. paniculata** Laxm.—China, Korea, and Japan. Specimen in BM. [Mss. at G] Introduction: about 1763 by G. W. Earl (Aiton, Hort. Kew., 1789).

EUCALYPTUS L'Hérit., Sert. Angl. 18. 1788 [1789]. Myrtaceae. T.: *E. obliqua* L'Hérit.

EUCALYPTUS OBLIQUA (p. 18, t. 20) [sp. nov.] = **E. obliqua** L'Hérit.—Australia. Specimens (type: Nelson, and Anderson, Australia) in BM. [Mss. at G] Introduction: 1774 by T. Furneaux (Aiton, Hort. Kew., 1789).

LAVANDULA L., Sp. Pl. 572. 1753. Labiatae. LT.: *L. spica* L.

LAVANDULA VIRIDIS (p. 19, t. 21) [sp. nov.] = **L. viridis** L'Hérit.—Madeira. Specimen (type: Masson, Madeira) in BM. [Mss. at G] Introduction: 1777 (Aiton, Hort. Kew., 1789).

BYSTROPOGON L'Hérit., Sert. Angl. 19. 1788 [1789]. Labiatae. T.: *B. suaveolens* (L.) L'Hérit. (*Ballota suaveolens* L.). = *Mesosphaerum* P. Browne 1756.

BYSTROPOGON PECTINATUM (p. 19) = **Hyptis pectinata** (L.) Poit.—Tropical America and West Indies. Specimens in BM. Introduction: 1776 by G. Alexander (Aiton, Hort. Kew., 1789).

BYSTROPOGON SIDAEFOLIUM (p. 19) [sp. nov.] = **Hyptis sidifolia** (L'Hérit.) Briq. (*H. polyantha* Poit.).—Peru. Specimen (type: Dombey, Peru) in BM. Introduction: 1819 (Loudon, Hort. Brit. 1830).

BYSTROPOGON SUAVEOLENS (p. 19) = **Hyptis suaveolens** (L.) Poit.—Tropical America. Specimens in BM. Introduction: 1800 (Loudon, Hort. Brit., 1830).

BYSTROPOGON PLUMOSUM (p. 20, t. 22) = **B. plumosus** (L.f.) L'Hérit.—Canary Islands. Specimen in BM. Introduction: 1779 (Aiton, Hort. Kew., 1789).

BYSTROPOGON ORIGANIFOLIUM (p. 20) [sp. nov.] = **B. origanifolius** L'Hérit.—Canary Islands. Specimen (type: Masson, Tenerife) in BM. Introduction: 1815 (Loudon, Hort. Brit., 1830).

BYSTROPOGON CANARIENSE (p. 20) = **B. canariensis** (L.) L'Hérit.—Madeira and Canary Islands. Specimens in BM. Introduction: 1714 (Loudon, Hort. Brit., 1830).

BYSTROPOGON PUNCTATUM (p. 20, t. 23) [sp. nov.] = **B. punctatus** L'Hérit.—Madeira. Specimens (type: Banks & Solander, and Masson, Madeira) in BM. Introduction: 1775 by J. Banks (Aiton, Hort. Kew., 1789).

DIGITALIS L., Sp. Pl. 621. 1753. Scrophulariaceae. LT.: *D. purpurea* L.

DIGITALIS SCEPTRUM L. (p. 21, t. 24) = **Isoplexis sceptrum** (L.f.) Steud.—Madeira. Specimen in BM. [Mss. at G] Introduction: 1777 (Aiton, Hort. Kew., 1789).

CAPRARIA L., Sp. Pl. 628. 1753. Scrophulariaceae. T.: *C. biflora* L.

CAPRARIA UNDULATA L.f. (p. 21, t. 25) = **Freylinia undulata** (L.f.) Benth.—South Africa. Specimens in BM. [Mss. at G] Introduction: 1774 (Aiton, Hort. Kew., 1789).

ASPALATHUS L., Sp. Pl. 711. 1753. Leguminosae. LT.: *A. chenopoda* L.

ASPALATHUS PEDUNCULATA (p. 21, t. 26) [sp. nov.] = **A. pedunculata** L'Hérit.—South Africa. Specimen (type: Masson, Cape of Good Hope) in BM. [Mss. at G] Introduction: 1775 (Aiton, Hort. Kew., 1789).

TANACETUM L., Sp. Pl. 843. 1753. Compositae. LT.: *T. vulgare* L.

TANACETUM FLABELLIFORME (p. 21, t. 27) [sp. nov.] = **Pentzia flabelliformis** (L'Hérit.) Willd.—South Africa. Specimens (type: Masson, Cape of Good Hope) in BM. [Mss. at G] Introduction: 1774 (Aiton, Hort. Kew., 1789).

ARTEMISIA L., Sp. Pl. 845. 1753. Compositae. LT.: *A. vulgaris* L.

ARTEMISIA ARGENTEA (p. 22, t. 28) [sp. nov.] = **A. argentea** L'Hérit.—Madeira. Specimen (type: Masson, Madeira) in BM. [Mss. at G] Introduction: 1777 (Aiton, Hort. Kew., 1789).

RELHANIA L'Hérit., Sert. Angl. 22. 1788 [1789]. Compositae. LT.: to be chosen.

RELHANIA SQUARROSA (p. 22, t. 29) = **R. squarrosa** (L.) L'Hérit.—South Africa. Specimens in BM. Introduction: 1774 by F. Masson (Aiton, Hort. Kew., 1789).

RELHANIA GENISTIFOLIA (p. 22) = **R. genistifolia** (L.) L'Hérit.—South Africa. Specimens in BM. Introduction: 1823 (Loudon, Hort. Brit., 1830).

RELHANIA MICROPHYLLA (p. 22) [sp. nov.] = **R. genistifolia** (L.) L'Hérit. var. **angustifolia** Harv. —South Africa. Specimen (type: Masson, Cape of Good Hope) in BM.

RELHANIA PASSERINOIDES (p. 23) [sp. nov.] = **R. passerinoides** L'Hérit.—South Africa. Specimen (type: Masson, Cape of Good Hope) in BM.

RELHANIA VISCOSA (p. 23) [sp. nov] = **R. passerinoides** L'Hérit. (*fide* S. Moore in Journ. Bot. 39: 386. 1901).—South Africa. Specimen (type: Masson, Cape of Good Hope) in BM.

RELHANIA LAXA (p. 23) [sp. nov.] = **R. laxa** L'Hérit.—South Africa. Specimen (type: Masson, Cape of Good Hope) in BM.

RELHANIA PEDUNCULATA (p. 23) [*nom. illegit.*] = **Ṙ. pumila** (L.f.) Thunb.—South Africa. Specimen in BM.

RELHANIA LATERIFLORA (p. 23) [*nom. illegit.*] = **R. sessiliflora** (L.f.) Thunb.—South Africa. Specimen in BM. Introduction: 1823 (Loudon, Hort. Brit., 1830).

RELHANIA CUNEATA (p. 23) [*nom. illegit.*] = **R. uniflora** (L.f.) Druce.—South Africa. Specimen in BM.

RELHANIA VIRGATA (p. 23) [sp. nov.] = **R. virgata** L'Hérit.—South Africa. Specimen (type: Masson, Cape of Good Hope) in BM.

RELHANIA PALEACEA (p. 24) = **R. paleacea** (L.) L'Hérit. (*R. ericoides* (Berg.) Cass. var. *paleacea* (L.) Harv.).—South Africa. Specimens in BM.

RELHANIA SANTOLINOIDES (p. 24) [sp. nov.] = **R. santolinoides** L'Hérit. (*R. ericoides* (Berg.) Cass. var. *santolinoides* (L'Hérit.) Harv.).—South Africa. Specimen (type: Masson, Cape of Good Hope) in BM.

RELHANIA PUNGENS (p. 24) [sp. nov.] = **R. pungens** L'Hérit.—South Africa. Specimen (type: Masson, Cape of Good Hope) in BM. Introduction: 1820 (Loudon, Hort. Brit., 1830).

RELHANIA DECUSSATA (p. 24) [sp. nov.] = **R. decussata** L'Hérit.—South Africa. Specimen (type: Masson, Cape of Good Hope) in BM.

Relhania calycina (p. 24) = **R. calycina** (L.f.) L'Hérit.—South Africa. Specimen in BM.

Relhania Bellidiastrum (p. 24) = **R. paleacea** (L.) L'Hérit. var. **bellidiastrum** (L.) S. Moore. —South Africa. Specimen in BM.

Cineraria L., Sp. Pl., ed. 2. 1242. 1764. [Mss. at G, including synopsis and notes on several species] Compositae. LT.: *C. geifolia* L.

Cineraria humifusa (p. 25) [sp. nov.] = **C. humifusa** L'Hérit.—South Africa. Specimen (type: Masson, Cape of Good Hope) in BM. Introduction: 1774 by F. Masson (Aiton, Hort. Kew., 1789).

Cineraria viscosa (p. 25) [sp. nov.] = **C. viscosa** L'Hérit.—South Africa. Specimen (type: Hort. Kew) in BM. Introduction: 1774 (Aiton, Hort. Kew., 1789).

Cineraria scapiflora (p. 25) [sp. nov.] = **C. scapiflora** L'Hérit.—South Africa. Specimens (type: Masson, Cape of Good Hope) in BM.

Cineraria mitellaefolia (p. 25) [*nom. illegit.*] = **Senecio cordifolius** L.f.—South Africa. Specimens in BM.

Cineraria lanata (p. 25, t. 30) [sp. nov.] = **Senecio heritieri** DC. (non *S. lanatus* Scop.).— Canary Islands. Specimen (type: Masson, Tenerife) in BM. Introduction: 1780 (Aiton, Hort. Kew., 1789).

Cineraria populifolia (p. 25) [*nom. illegit.*] = **Senecio appendiculatus** (L.f.) Schultz Bip.— —Canary Islands. Specimen in BM. Introduction: 1780 (Aiton, Hort. Kew., 1789).

Cineraria aurita (p. 26, t. 31) [sp. nov.] = **Senecio maderensis** DC. (non *S. auritus* Willd.)— Madeira. Specimen (type: Masson, Madeira) in BM. Introduction: 1777 (Aiton, Hort. Kew., 1789).

Cineraria ramentosa (p. 26) [*nom. illegit.*] = **Senecio echinatus** (L.f.) DC.—Canary Islands. Specimen in BM.

Cineraria malvaefolia (p. 26, t. 32) [sp. nov.] = **Senecio malvifolius** (L'Hérit.) DC.—Azores and Canary Islands. Specimens (type: Masson, Azores and Canary Islands) in BM. Introduction: 1777 (Aiton, Hort. Kew., 1789).

Cineraria multiflora (p. 26) [sp. nov.] = **Senecio multiflorus** (L'Hérit.) DC.—Canary Islands. Specimen (type: Masson, Canary Islands) in BM.

Cineraria cruenta (p. 26, t. 33) [sp. nov.] = **Senecio cruentus** (L'Hérit.) DC.—Canary Islands. Specimen (type: Masson, Tenerife) in BM. Introduction: 1777 by F. Masson (Aiton, Hort. Kew., 1789).

Cineraria tussilaginis (p. 26) [sp. nov.] = **Senecio tussilaginis** (L'Hérit.) Less.—Canary Islands. Specimen (type: Masson, Tenerife) in BM. Introduction: about 1832 (Bot. Mag. t. 3215. 1833).

Cineraria lobata (p. 26, t. 34) [sp. nov.] = **C. lobata** L'Hérit.—South Africa. Specimen (type: Banks & Solander, Cape of Good Hope) in BM. Introduction: 1774 (Aiton, Hort. Kew., 1789).

Cineraria senecionis (p. 27) [sp. nov.] = **C. senecionis** L'Hérit.—South Africa.

BOLTONIA L'Hérit., Sert. Angl. 27. 1788 [1789]. Compositae. LT.: *B. asteroides* (L.) L'Hérit. *(Matricaria asteroides* L.)

> BOLTONIA GLASTIFOLIA (p. 27, t. 35 [not published]) = **B. asteroides** (L.) L'Hérit. var. **glastifolia** (J. Hill) Fern.—E. United States. Specimen in BM. [Mss. at G] Introduction: 1758 (Loudon, Hort. Brit., 1830).

> BOLTONIA ASTEROIDES (p. 27, t. 36 [not published]) = **B. asteroides** (L.) L'Hérit.—E. United States. Specimen in BM. [Mss. at G] Introduction: 1758 (Loudon, Hort. Brit., 1830).

BUPHTHALMUM L., Sp. Pl. 903. 1753. Compositae. LT.: *B. salicifolium* L.

> BUPHTHALMUM SERICEUM (p. 27, t. 37 [not published]) = **Odontospermum sericeum** (L.f.) Schultz Bip.—Canary Islands. Specimen in BM. [Mss. at G] Introduction: 1779 (Aiton, Hort. Kew., 1789).

STOKESIA L'Hérit., Sert. Angl. 27. 1788 [1789]. Compositae. T.: *S. cyanea* L'Hérit. *[nom. illegit.]* = *S. laevis* (J. Hill) Greene, *Carthamus laevis* J. Hill.

> STOKESIA CYANEA (p. 28, t. 38 [not published]) *[nom. illegit.]* = **S. laevis** (J. Hill) Greene.—S. E. United States. Specimens in G. (type: in Prod. Herb.) and in BM. [Mss. at G] Introduction: about 1766 by J. Gordon (Aiton, Hort. Kew., 1789).

LIMODORUM L., Sp. Pl. 950. 1953. Orchidaceae. T.: *L. tuberosum* L.

> LIMODORUM TANCARVILLEAE (p. 28) [sp. nov.] = **Phaius tancarvilleae** (Banks ex L'Hérit.) Blume.—N. India and S. China through Malaysia to Australia and the Pacific. Introduction: about 1778 by J. Fothergill (Aiton, Hort. Kew., 1789).

> LIMODORUM TUBEROSUM L. (p. 28) = *L. tuberosum* L'Hérit. (non L.) = **Calopogon pulchellus** (Salisb.) R. Br.—N. America, Cuba, and Bahamas. Specimen in BM. Introduction: 1787 by W. Curtis (Aiton, Hort. Kew., 1789).

> LIMODORUM ALTUM L. (p. 28) = *L. altum* l'Hérit. (non L.) = **Bletia purpurea** (Lam.) DC.—Florida, C. America, West Indies. Specimen in BM. Introduction: before 1733 by W. Houston (Aiton, Hort. Kew., 1789).

GENESIPHYLLA L'Hérit., Sert. Angl. 29. 1788 [1789]. Euphorbiaceae. T.: *G. asplenifolia* L'Hérit.

> GENESIPHYLLA ASPLENIFOLIA (p. 29, t. 39 [not published]) *[nom. illegit.]* = **Phyllanthus latifolius** (L.) Sw.—Jamaica. Specimen in BM. [Mss. at G] Introduction: 1783 (Loudon, Hort. Brit., 1830, sub *Xylophylla latifolia*).

TAMUS L., Sp. Pl. 1028. 1753. Dioscoriaceae. L.T.: *T. communis* L.

> TAMUS ELEPHANTIPES (p. 29, t. 40 [not published]) [sp. nov.] = **Testudinaria elephantipes** (L'Hérit.) Salisb.—South Africa. Specimen (? type: Nelson, Cape of Good Hope, ex Horto) in BM. Introduction: 1774 (Aiton, Hort. Kew., 1789).

MIMOSA L., Sp. Pl. 516. 1753. Leguminosae. LT.: *M. pudica* L.

> MIMOSA VERTICILLATA (p. 30, t. 41 [not published]) [sp. nov.] = **Acacia verticillata** (L'Hérit.)

Willd.—Australia. Specimen (type: Nelson, Tasmania) in BM. [Mss. at G] Introduction: 1780 by J. Banks (Aiton, Hort. Kew., 1789).

MIMOSA HOUSTONI (p. 30) [*nom. illegit.*] = **Calliandra houstoniana** (Mill.) Standley.—C. America. Specimen (type: from Miller Herbarium via Banks) in G. Introduction: 1729 (Bot. Reg. t. 98. 1816).

MIMOSA GRANDIFLORA (p. 30, t. 42 [not published]) [sp. nov.] = **Calliandra grandiflora** (L'Hérit.) Benth.—Tropical America. [Mss. at G] Introduction: about 1769 by Mrs. Norman (Aiton, Hort. Kew., 1789).

DICKSONIA L'Hérit., Sert. Angl. 30. 1788 [1789]. Dicksoniaceae (sometimes included in Cyatheaceae). LT.: *D. arborescens* L'Hérit.

DICKSONIA ARBORESCENS (p. 31, t. 43 [not published]) [sp. nov.] = **D. arborescens** L'Hérit.—St. Helena. Specimen (type: Banks, St. Helena) in BM. Introduction: 1786 by A. Hove (Aiton, Hort. Kew., 1789).

DICKSONIA CULCITA (p. 31) [sp. nov.] = **Culcita macrocarpa** Presl.—Azores, Madeira, Canary Islands. Specimen (type: Masson, Azores) in BM. [Mss. at G] Introduction: 1779 (Aiton, Hort. Kew., 1789).

EUCLEA L. in Murr., Syst. 746. 1774. Ebenaceae. T.: *E. racemosa* L.

EUCLEA RACEMOSA L. (p. 32) = *E. racemosa* L'Hérit. (non L.) = **Kiggelaria dregeana** Turcz. var. **obtusa** Harv. (*fide* Hiern in Harvey & Sonder, Fl. Cap. 4 (1): 474. 1909) (Flacourtiaceae).—South Africa. Specimen in BM.

LIST OF COLLECTORS CITED IN THE SERTUM ANGLICUM

ADANSON, Michel [1727-1806]
Senegał 1749-1753. Herbarium at P. French scientist who worked in Senegal from 1749-1753; author of *Familles des Plantes* (1763).

ANDERSON, William [? -1778]
Horticulturist who went with Cook on his second (1772-1775) and third (1776-1780) voyages. Plants at BM. Died at sea during Cook's third voyage on 3 August 1778.

AUGÉ, Johann Andreas (Jan Andries) [1711-1796]
Collected at the Cape between 1747?-1796; cooperated with C. P. Thunberg when the latter visited the Cape. Plants at BM, G, L, LINN, SBT.

BANKS, Joseph [1743-1820]
Leading British scientist of the period; accompanied Cook on his first voyage. Herbarium at BM.

BRUGUIÈRE(s), Jean-Guillaume [1750-1798]
Franch traveller, especially at the Cape, Madagascar, Réunion, Mauritius. Plants at P in the de Jussieu herbarium. Made drawing for *Amaryllis spiralis*, used by L'Héritier, original now at BM (see p. *lxiv*).

COMMERSON, Philibert [1727-1773]
French traveller with de Bougainville on his circumnavigation 1766-1769, also in Madagascar 1770-1771, Mauritius 1769-1773 (with interruptions), and Réunion 1771. Herbarium at P, duplicates in many herbaria including BM, G, LINN.

DOMBEY, Joseph [1742-1793]
French botanist and traveller who collected widely in Peru and Chile (1778-84), as well as in Brazil (1784), and in France. The Dombey affair was responsible for L'Héritier's visit to England, out of which came his *Sertum Anglicum*. Plants at P but also at many other herbaria including BM, CGE, G, K, L, MO, MPU, NY).

FORSTER, Johann Georg Adam [1754-1794]
Son of Johann Reinhold Forster (1729-1798), whom he accompanied on Cook's second voyage (1772-1775). Plants at BM (main set), GOET, LINN, and some at P and K.

GARDEN, Alexander [1730?-1791]
Physician and botanist born in Charleston, S.C., graduate of University of Edinburgh 1748, returned as a physician to Charleston, S.C. in 1752. Correspondent of Bartram, Linnaeus, Ellis, Collinson, and others. Returned to England in 1783.

HOUSTON, William [1695?-1733] (Sometimes spelled Houstoun).
Scottish physician who collected in Central America and the West Indies until about 1727, when he studied under Boerhaave at Leiden for two years and returned to the Caribbean region until his death at Jamaica in 1733. Banks acquired his plants, drawings, and notes. Plants at BM (original set), CGE, LINN, OXF, P, etc.

HULTGREN, Matthias [?]
A collector of unknown identity who sent plants from Maryland (U.S.A.) to England.

KOENIG, Johann Gerhard [1728-1785]
Danish pupil of Linnaeus, physician and naturalist, travelled in Iceland 1765, in India 1768-1785. Bequeathed plants and manuscripts to Banks, now at BM. In India he was employed by the Danish mission at Tranquebar as surgeon and naturalist (1768-1774); in 1774 he entered the service of the Nabob of Arcot; in 1778 until his death he was naturalist to the East India Company.

LIND, James [1736-1812]
English physician, astronomer, and cartographer, visited China and India 1766-67 as surgeon in an East Indiaman, and accompanied Sir Joseph Banks to Iceland in 1772.

MASSON, Francis [1741-1806]
First plant collector sent from Kew. Collected at the Cape 1772-1773, in the Canaries and Azores 1778-1782, in Spain and Portugal 1783-1785, again at the Cape (with Thunberg) 1786-1795, and in North America 1798. Plants at BM.

NELSON, David [? -1789]
Kew gardener who, as "assistant botanist," collected for Banks on Cook's third voyage 1776-1780. Accompanied Captain Bligh on the voyage of the Bounty in 1787-1789, remaining with Bligh's party in the cutter, but died soon after having reached Timor. Plants at BM. It was Nelson who collected a specimen of *Eucalyptus obliqua*, a species first described by L'Héritier.

OLDENBURG, Fredrik Peter [? -1774]
Collected for Kew at the Cape circa 1771-1773; sent about 1,000 specimens to Banks, now at BM.

POIVRE, Pierre [1719-1786]
French missionary to China and Indo-china (1739-1748); subsequently traveller for the French East India Company to Cochin China, the Moluccas, the Philippines, Madagascar and elsewhere (1749-1757). Plants at P.

SOLANDER, Daniel Carl [1736-1782]
Pupil of Linnaeus, came to England in 1760. Accompanied Banks as botanist on Cook's first voyage (1768-1771), and on excursion to Iceland (1772); Bank's librarian 1771-1782.

THUNBERG, Carolus Petrus (Carl Pehr) [1743-1828]
Swedish botanist and traveller, pupil of Linnaeus, prolific botanical author. Travelled in South Africa from 1772-1775, in Java, Ceylon, and Japan 1775-1779. Succeeded Linnaeus *filius* as professor of botany at Uppsala in 1784. Plants at UPS, duplicates at L, LINN, S, SBT, and other herbaria.

WRIGHT, William [1735-1819]
Scottish physician and traveller, to Greenland 1757, to Jamaica 1765, 1777, and 1779-1785, and to Barbados 1796-1798. Plants at BM.

The illustrators of Sertum Anglicum

Wilfrid Blunt

Two draughtsmen—the Belgian-born Pierre-Joseph Redouté and the Englishman James Sowerby—joined forces to produce the drawings for all but three of the plates for L'Héritier's *Sertum Anglicum*. Both artists were young men, in their late twenties at the time, relatively inexperienced and with reputations still to be made; both were to achieve fame, and one of them world-wide popularity also, as illustrators of botanical works.

Pierre-Joseph Redouté was born in the Walloon village of St. Hubert in the Ardennes in 1795 (then in Luxembourg, now Belgium). The second of three brothers, he came of a long line of Belgian painters, and both his brothers also adopted art as a profession. Young Pierre-Joseph, after learning the basic elements of his craft under his father, gained a living for a time as an itinerant painter and then studied briefly but more seriously in Liège. It was probably a sight, during his *Wanderjahren*, of some of the works of Rachel Ruysch and Jan van Huysum at Amsterdam that turned his steps in the direction of flower-painting.

In 1782 he joined his elder brother, Antoine-Ferdinand, in Paris. Here his interest in flowers led him to the Jardin du Roi, where he attracted the attention of L'Héritier, whose pupil he became. L'Héritier's fine library and his botanical knowledge were generously put at his disposal, and the young man, almost without being aware of it, had set his foot upon the first rung of the ladder of success. L'Héritier soon considered him competent to assist him in his botanical publications, and more than fifty of the engravings in *Stirpes novae* (1784-85) are from drawings by Pierre-Joseph. When L'Héritier fled to England in 1786, Redouté joined him there for a few months and, in collaboration with James Sowerby, made the bulk of the drawings that illustrate *Sertum Anglicum*

While L'Héritier acted as Redouté's botanical mentor, Gerard van Spaendonck guided his artistic progress. Van Spaendonck (1746-1822) was a Dutchman who, like Redouté, had come to Paris to seek his fortune and had been appointed *Professeur de peinture des fleurs* at the Museum of the Jardin du Roi. Even more greatly gifted by nature than Redouté, he was less fortunate than his pupil in finding patronage; his output was small and his name is not so well known to the general public.

For it was the patronage of the Empress Joséphine which gave Redouté an opportunity that had never before, and has never since, come the way of a botanical artist. Joséphine adored flowers, and she engaged Redouté, at a salary of 18,000 francs a year, to work for her. Ventenat's *Jardin de la Malmaison* (1803-05) and Bonpland's *Description des plantes rares cultivées à Malmaison et à Navarre* (1812-17), both illustrated with magnificent coloured engravings after paintings by Redouté, are among the most splendid flower

Reproduction of original drawing of *Hippeastrum vittatum* (*Amaryllis vittata*) by Redouté, reproduced in *Sertum Anglicum* in Pl. 15

books ever produced. *Les liliacées* (1802-16) is another work illustrated by Redouté at the height of his power. The later *Les roses* (1817-24), and especially his *Choix des plus belles fleurs* (1827-33), are more "fashionable" in intention; lovely though they both are, and highly as they are prized by collectors, they do not appeal to botanists so strongly as do the works of Redouté's middle period.

Redouté made big money and for a time lived in style; but he was not the man to save for a rainy day. His affairs went from bad to worse, and his furniture, silver, and paintings had to be sold. On June 19th, 1840, while examining a white lily brought him by a pupil, he had a stroke. He died the following day, at the age of 81.

James Sowerby (1757-1822) was the first, and the most distinguished, of a large family many of whose members illustrated books on natural history subjects from the closing years of the eighteenth century onwards. Descended from the Yorkshire branch of an old Border family, he trained at the Royal Academy Schools and became an articled pupil of the marine painter, Richard Wright. After Wright's death, about 1775, Sowerby seems to have earned his livelihood for a time by teaching drawing and by painting portraits; but flower-painting aroused his interest and soon led him to the study of botany.

It would appear that L'Héritier was the first botanist to make use of his talent in this field; Sowerby was at this time nearly thirty, and for the remaining thirty-four years of his life he worked unremittingly as an illustrator of books on natural history. He was elected an Associate of the Linnean Society in 1788, and five years later became a Fellow. Zoology, mineralogy, and conchology, especially that branch of the last-named science that deals with fossil shells, became during the later part of his life his major interest. A son, grandson, and great-grandson, all named George Brettingham Sowerby, specialized in the painting of conchological subjects. His eldest son, James de Carle Sowerby, devoted himself to botanical and conchological illustration, and the interest of another grandson, John Edward Sowerby, was principally botanical.

Among the most important works illustrated wholly or in part by Sowerby are: *English botany* (1790-1814), the *Botanical magazine* (seventy or more plates in the first four volumes), Curtis's *Flora Londinensis* (about fifty plates in the fifth fasciculus), Sir James Edward Smith's *Icones pictae plantarum rariorum* (1790-93), Aiton's *Hortus Kewensis* (1789), and two works of his own—*An easy introduction to drawing flowers according to nature* (1788) and *Flora luxurians* ([1789]-91). It was of the last-named that he remarked, with characteristic modesty, "As all the Productions of the Earth were designed for the Amusement or Convenience of its Inhabitants: the most humble Attempt to display the Beauties of Nature should not be despised by those who, wrapped up in their own Pursuits, think every other insignificant."

Probably Sowerby would have continued his association with the *Botanical magazine* had he not taken on the vast task of making the illustrations—nearly 2,500 in number— for the *English botany*, the text of which was provided by Sir James Edward Smith. There was also another great undertaking—*Coloured figures of English fungi*—which occupied him, on and off, from 1797 till 1815. For this he also wrote the text, and made some two hundred models of British fungi. His skill as an engraver is shown in the plates of

Reproduction of original drawing of *Carpolyza tenella* (*Amaryllis spiralis*) by Bruguière, reproduced in *Sertum Anglicum* in Pl. 13

Sibthorp's superb *Flora Graeca,* the majority of which were engraved by him from the drawings of the great Ferdinand Bauer.

Sowerby died in his house at Lambeth on October 25th, 1822.

Three plates remain to be considered; the drawings for two of these are the work of J.-G. Bruguière, and that for the third is by Pernotin. Jean-Guillaume Bruguière, botanical artist, traveller, and collector, was born in Montpellier in 1750 and died in 1798 or 1799. He travelled in the Cape Province, Madagascar, Réunion, and Mauritius, and his specimens are in the de Jussieu Herbarium in Paris. The original drawings for his two plates in *Sertum Anglicum* (pls. 13 and 17) are preserved in the British Museum (Natural History), London, and, of them, that of L'Héritier's *Amaryllis spiralis* [*Carpolyza tenella* (L.f.) Leighton] is here reproduced. They are neat, painstaking sketches in monochrome wash, adequate for their purpose but of no great artistic value.

The artist Pernotin cannot be identified with certainty, since no initials are given on the plate (pl. 14) for which he made the drawing. It is, however, highly probably that he was B. Pernotin, a Frenchman who was working in London between 1786 and 1797. B. Pernotin was a painter of historical subjects, genre, and portraits, among the last mentioned being one of Swedenborg which was engraved by Miss Martin.

As has already been pointed out, both Redouté and Sowerby were at the very beginning of their careers when they made the drawings for *Sertum Anglicum.* None of Sowerby's original drawings for this book survives, but two of those by Redouté, (*Amaryllis aurea* and *A. vittata*—both here reproduced) are now in the Rachel McMasters Miller Hunt Botanical Library. They are painted with the greatest care and attention to botanical detail, but they inevitably lack the subtlety and refinement of his more mature work and the brilliance that full colour always provides. Moreover, few of the plants allotted to L'Héritier's artists were of a spectacular kind, and only those shown in plates 11, 14, 15, 15 *bis,* 16, 18, and 24 gave scope for decorative treatment. This fact, combined with the absence of colour, has naturally prevented *Sertum Anglicum* from ranking with *Les roses* and the *Choix des plus belles fleurs* among those fine books for which collectors are today willing to pay enormous sums in the sale-room. It is, in brief, a botanists' book.

The plates for *Sertum Anglicum* were engraved in France, and of the six craftsmen employed there is little that needs to be said. Pierre Maleuvre (1740-1803), a Parisian, engraved eleven of the drawings, and François Hubert (1744-1809) was responsible for ten more. They were conscientious, uninspired craftsmen who adequately performed the functions for which they were employed—namely, to make the facts of a single drawing available to a larger audience. Jacques Juillet (born 1739), who engraved six plates, had a slightly greater reputation; he was also responsible for carrying out the plates used to illustrate J. Pillement's *Recueil de différents bouquets.* Jean-Baptiste Guyard (five plates) was probably the father of the later engraver of the same name, some of whose work can be traced. Of the remaining two, Stephan Voysard (two plates) and Milsan (one plate), nothing has been discovered. The engraving throughout the whole volume was hack-work, which today would be done more satisfactorily by mechanical means.

It is of significance in the field of botanical illustration that in L'Héritier de Brutelle's *Sertum Anglicum* thirty-one of the thirty-five plates depict for the first time the species represented (only the species shown in plates 2, 19, 26, and 30 are known to have been illustrated previously in any botanical volume). It is also significant that in this work seven of the species first illustrated here have never been illustrated subsequently (the species shown in plates 6, 16, 17, 22, 23, 29, and 32). The botanical importance of those plates, and the taxonomic utility of the volume, are thereby increased.

An English translation of *Sertum Anglicum*

L'Héritier de Brutelle wrote his *Sertum Anglicum* wholly in Latin. Even at that time, only the finest productions of botanical works were written in Latin, although in earlier times Latin was the universal language for works in natural history.

The recognition that while twentieth-century taxonomic botanists do read Latin narratives readily, and that few other botanists, horticulturists, or bibliophiles do so, prompts the inclusion of an English translation of all portions of the text except the Latin names themselves, including polynomials, and the conventional Latin descriptions of the genera and species. For the latter, knowledge of English botanical terminology, substantially unchanged from the Latin, makes it possible for any taxonomist to comprehend descriptive passages. The translation given on the following pages is restricted primarily to the author's notes accounting for the origin or history of each plant, his discussions of a plant's diagnostic features, and his explanations of its relationships, nomenclature, and cultural requirements. In the translation, L'Héritier's spelling of Latin names of plants is retained without regard for correctness according to modern rules.

This translation has been prepared by a trio of Benedictine Fathers at Saint Vincent Archabbey, Latrobe, Pennsylvania:

Rev. Maximilian Duman O.S.B.
President of St. Vincent College and botanical
specialist of arctic floras and the genus Carex

Rev. Leopold Kral O.S.B.
Prior of the Archabbey and Professor of Latin

Rev. Rembert Weakland O.S.B.
Organist and Professor of Mediaeval Musicology

CHARLES LOUIS L'HÉRITIER, DOM. DE BRUTELLE

Royal Counsellor at the Paris Court of Public Revenue

AN ENGLISH WREATH

OR

RARE PLANTS

WHICH ARE CULTIVATED IN THE

GARDENS AROUND LONDON

ESPECIALLY

IN THE ROYAL GARDENS AT KEW

OBSERVED

FROM THE YEAR 1786 TO THE YEAR 1787

PARIS

PRINTED BY PIERRE-FRANÇOIS DIDOT

To be sold at
PARIS, *by* LOUIS-NICOLAS PRÉVOST
THEOPHIL. BARROIS
LONDON, *by* PETER ELMSLY
VIENNA & LEIPSIG, *by* RUDOLF GRAEFFER
STRASBURG, *by* AMAND. KOENIG

1788

To my botanist reader, greetings!

The celebrity of her gardens brought me to England, and especially that live herbarium of Linnaeus, famous for its excellence and erected to the immortal fame of that outstanding man as well as for the continued study of botany.

Working without respite for fifteen months, I took care to place these most valuable plants in their proper genera—not without great admiration for the gardens, justly famous for the abundance of their plants and for the diligence with which they are tended.

In this present collection are gathered the choice and rare plants, certainly a most fruitful harvest that pays back with interest the inconvenience of my travels! The remaining ones I reserve for other works, in which specific features of each one will be outlined along with congeneric plants.

I dedicate and offer in a special way this list of her plants to the English nation. For praise ought to redound to its source. A deep spirit of gratitude that will always fall short of what I have gained also prompts me. I am happy to relate, and I love to remember, how courteously everyone received me; how the scholars showed themselves accommodating and ready to reveal their treasures; how especially the men so learned in botany assisted me obligingly.

May then the English Botanists, and they alone, receive this little work in which I have described the new genera as a gift, not unwelcome I hope, nor insignificant. May they look with approval upon my labor; and may I take the liberty of showing myself grateful and eternally mindful by this work—distinguished and made illustrious with their name. Given at Paris, on the 20th of April, 1788.

[p. 1]

SYNOPTICAL ACCOUNT

Plants with flowers having four stamens

WITHERINGIA

WITHERINGIA *solanacea*. Plate 1.
    Native in... [unknown]. Plant a perennial herb.

CHLORANTHUS

CHLORANTHUS *inconspicuus*. Plate 2.
    Common name in China: Tchu-lan
    Native of China. A woody plant.

Plants with flowers having five stamens

PRISMATOCARPUS
[Synonyms are:] *Specularia* Heister, *Legousia* Durande

Although it seems best, from the nature of the species, to keep the genus *Prismatocarpus*, perhaps it should not be retained, however, since it has the true characters of *Campanula*. I hope to confirm or weaken this opinion of mine by new observations before the drawing of *P. nitidus* is published.

Many illustrious botanists have thought that *Prismatocarpus* should be distinguished from the genus Campanula. Haller (in *Historia Stirpium* vol. 1, p. 311, [1768]) when treating *Campanula specula*, uses these words: "it is truly something other than a *Campanula*." Scopoli (in *Flora Carniolica* vol. 1, p. 150, [1760]) says about this same plant: "flower with five petals, rotate, expanded, and entirely outside the genus."

[p. 2] 1. PRISMATOCARPUS *interruptus*
Native on the promontory at Cape of Good Hope. [Specimens collected by] Thunberg [and] Oldenburg.

2. PRISMATOCARPUS *paniculatus*
Native on the promontory at Cape of Good Hope. [Specimen collected by] Andreas Augé.
Calyces [*i.e.*, calyx-lobes] linear, very sharply acute.
Linnaeus certainly recognized *Polemonium roëlloides* with its columnar, inferior ovary as the genus [I am designating as] *Prismatocarpus*, but I failed when I was visiting England to compare it [that species] with examples of [this] new genus.

3. PRISMATOCARPUS *altiflorus*
Native of Cape Town, Cape of Good Hope. [Specimen collected by] Fr[ancis] Masson.
[The species] *P. interruptus, paniculatus* and *altiflorus* are alike with [*i.e.*, in having] the leaves and habit of *Lepidium subulatum*. The muricate-ciliate margins of the leaves [in these species] have somewhat more rigid teeth.

4. PRISMATOCARPUS *fruticosus*
Native on the promontory at Cape of Good Hope. [Specimen collected by Francis] Masson. A woody plant.

5. PRISMATOCARPUS *crispus*
Native on the promontory at Cape of Good Hope. [Specimens collected by Andreas] Augé [and by Francis] Masson.
Calices subulate. Leaves with revolute margins and [are] villose [shaggy-hairy] as is the stem. It certainly has the appearance of *Campanula undulata*, which is very distinct with its short conical ovary, as in other [species of] *Campanula*.

6. PRISMATOCARPUS *nitidus*. Plate 3.

Native on the promontory at Cape of Good Hope. [Specimen collected by Francis] Masson.

It bears a very strong resemblance to *Jussiaea*.

It differs from the related genera, which are characterized by a sessile flower and the stems fruiting at the base.

[p. 3] 7. PRISMATOCARPUS *Speculum*

Native of the central and southern regions of Europe. Plant an annual herb.

The calices are longer than [in] all [other species], lanceolate in younger plants, linear in older ones.

8. PRISMATOCARPUS *hybridus*

Native of the regions of Switzerland, England, France, Jugoslavia (Serbo-Croatia). Plant an annual herb.

9. PRISMATOCARPUS *Pentagonia*

Native of Greece (Thrace). Plant an annual herb.

Plant one foot high, branching, pubescent. The lower leaves resembling those of *Bellida,* petiolate, [the margins] nearly entire or slightly crenulate; those [leaves] on the stem subsessile, obversely oblong [oblanceolate?), nearly entire; those on the branches sessile, oblong or lanceolate, [with apices] rounded. Flowers somewhat larger [than in other species]. Pistils [germina] longer than the corolla. Calyx [lobes] linear, acute, slightly pilose, flat but [the margins] not revolute as in *P. Speculum.*

[p. 4] ## LIGHTFOOTIA

[This genus] differs from Campanula by the five-petalled corolla, as well as by the multivalved capsule.

1. LIGHTFOOTIA *oxycoccoides*. Plate 4.

Native on the promontory at Cape of Good Hope. [Specimen collected by Francis] Masson. Plant a perennial herb.

2. LIGHTFOOTIA *subulata*. Plate 5.

Native on the promontory at Cape of Good Hope. [Specimen collected by Francis] Masson.

ROËLLA

ROËLLA *decurrens*. Plate 6.

Native of Cape Town, Cape of Good Hope. [Specimen collected by Francis] Masson. Plant an annual herb.

HAMELIA

1. HAMELIA *patens* L.

    Native of Haiti and Santo Domingo (Hispaniola). A woody plant.

2. HAMELIA *grandiflora*. Plate 7.

    Native of Jamaica. A woody plant.

[p. 5]

RHAMNUS

[Footnote below description:] By analogy one could designate the squamulae of Linnaeus' *Rhamnus* as petals. This has been determined from [the situation in] *Ceanothus* and also in *R. Zizyphus* and in *Paliurus*.

1. RHAMNUS *hybridus*

    Known only from gardens. A woody plant.

    I obtained this plant more than ten years ago from seeds of *R. alpinus*. The mother [plant] was entirely pistillate and for a number of years was isolated from [pollination by] male plants. *R. alaternus* was certainly the male parent. The seeds were sown in several regions of France and consistently produced a hybrid plant which was not a sport.

    [This hybrid] has characteristics [Latin *tenet* = French *tient*] of both parents. The vegetative growth resembles the seed parent. The leaves are intermediate between those of *R. alpinus* and *alaternus*, in texture closest to *R. alaternus* but are almost perennial [*i.e.*, the foliage is nearly evergreen]. The flowers are androgynous, as in the male parent, and are not unisexual as in the seed parent.

2. RHAMNUS *alnifolius*

    Native of North America. A woody plant.

    This species is similar in appearance to *R. alpinus*, but the leaves are more laxly nerved, more strongly reticulate, and are only glabrous and not glossy as in *R. alpinus*.

3. RHAMNUS *volubilis* L.

    Native of [South] Carolina. [Specimen collected by Dr. Alexander] Garden [of Charleston, S.C.] and Louisiana. A woody plant.

    R. volubilis and *lineatus* are somewhat alike. Both have flowers with petaloid scales of *Rhamnus*, and double-seeded drupes with bilocular interior of *Cornus*.

4. RHAMNUS *latifolius*. Plate 8.

[p. 6]

    Native of the mountains of St. Miguel, in the Azores. [Specimen collected by Francis] Masson. A woody plant.

    It is very similar to *R. Frangula*, but larger; it has villose calices, which in *R. Frangula* are glabrous; its petaloid scales are sessile, while in *R. Frangula* they are somewhat unguiculate [tongue-shaped].

5. RHAMNUS *prinoides*. Plate 9.

Native on the promontory at Cape of Good Hope. [Specimens collected by Andreas] Augé [and by Francis] Masson. A woody plant.

6. RHAMNUS *micranthus* L. will become *Celtis micrantha* in my flora of Peru.

CEANOTHUS

CEANOTHUS *reclinatus*

Native of Jamaica. [Specimen collected by] William Wright. A woody plant.

Because of the dry fruit that is definitely [that] of the *Ceanothus,* and the arched petals which are shorter than the *C. americanus,* I would rather place this [plant] in *Ceanothus* than in *Rhamnus;* however, the entire genus *Ceanothus* should more correctly be included in *Rhamnus.*

CELASTRUS

1. CELASTRUS *corniculatus*

    Native on the promontory at Cape of Good Hope. A woody plant. Similar to species of *Euclea.*

2. CELASTRUS *cassinoides.* Plate 10.

    Native in the Madeira Islands. [Specimen collected by Francis] Masson. A woody plant.

3. CELASTRUS *phyllacanthus*

[p. 7]   Native in Senegal. [Specimen collected by Michel] Adanson.

    The plant is growing in the Royal Botanic Garden, Paris, but it has not yet produced any fruit.

4. CELASTRUS *octogonus*

    Native in Peru. [Specimen collected by Joseph] Dombey. A woody plant.

    The leaves are glaucous. The flowers are usually polygamous, or very rarely bisexual or pistillate. The seeds bear an aril which is divided into two lobes. There are other species of Peru and Chile which also have only a bi-valvate capsule.

5. CELASTRUS *undulatus*

    Common name in France: *Bois de joli coeur.*

    Native of the Isle de Reunion. [Specimen collected by] Phil[ibert] Com-merson. A woody plant.

    [Distinguished by] its leaves lanceolate, [the apices] acuminate, slightly one-nerved, [the surface] undulate, the revolute margins white. Petals spatulate-shaped. Stigma slightly capitate. Capsule unilocular, bivalved, many-seeded. The seeds 8-12, naked and not arillate.

    Plant used as an antisyphilitic [according to] Commerson.

    It differs slightly from Ceanothus by its pericarp [the naked seed coat] and [number of] seeds, but not sufficiently so as to constitute a new genus.

It once grew in the Royal Botanic Garden, Paris, but is now in the nursery of James Lee, an English gardener.

Plants with flowers having six stamens

PITCAIRNIA

Pitcairnia *bromeliaefolia*. Plate 11.
Native in Jamaica. A perennial herb.
A genus that is intermediate between *Bromelia* and *Tillandsia*.

[p. 8]

TRADESCANTIA

Tradescantia *discolor*
Native of tropical America. Plant a perennial herb.

CRINUM

The distinctive character [of this genus] is found in the cylindrical [perianth-] tube, and in the equal [lobes of the] limb. It differs from *Pancratium* only in the absence of the nectary.

1. Crinum *asiaticum* L.
   Native of Malabar [India], Ceylon, Tranquebar [a town on Coromandel coast], tropical America. Plant a perennial herb.
   Stamens somewhat declined.
2. Crinum *americanum* L.
   Native of Tropical America.
3. Crinum *nervosum*
   Native of the Philippine Islands. [Specimen collected by Pierre] Poivre.

[p. 9] The leaves are rounded with a heart-shaped base, the margins are entire, [apices] acuminate, [the blade] veined with concentric veins, the scape many-flowered, many-bracted. The flowers are long-stalked. The corollas are funnelshaped, the [perianth-] tube very slender, the limb six-lobed, the fringe-segments lanceolate, acute, spreading. The [stamen] filaments arise from the throat, are opposite to and shorter than the fringe-segments, broad and ample at the base, free [from one another], erect, not declined— as it would seem to me.

Crinum latifolium L. is *Amaryllis latifolia*
———— *zeylanicum* L. is *Amaryllis zeylanica*

[*lxxv*]

Crinum africanum L. is *Agapanthus umbellatus*

—— *tenellum* L. is *Leucoium* in the opinion of Linnaeus [*Species Plantarum*, ed.]
  2 vol. i and of [Daniel] Solander, or is perhaps a new genus.

—— *obliquum* L. is *Amaryllis umbrella* [error for *umbella*]

—— *speciosum* L. is *Amaryllis speciosa*

—— *lineare* L. is unknown to me

—— *angustifolium* L. is *Amaryllis cylindracea*

—— *falcatum* Jacq. is *Amaryllis falcata*

AMARYLLIS

The direction [of growth] or the unequal proportion of the filaments suggests the essential [diagnostic feature] of the genus.

* [Species in which] the corollas are regular, the filaments alternate [with] and are shorter [than the segments]

1. AMARYLLIS *lutea* L.

    Native of Montpellier [France], Spain, Italy, northern Greece. Plant a perennial herb.

    This [species] differs slightly from the genus.

2. AMARYLLIS *tubispatha*

    Native of Buenos Aires. [Specimens collected by Philibert] Commerson.

    [p. 10] The scape [primary flower stalk] is one-flowered, erect, four inches high. The spatha is one-half to almost as long as the scape, cylindrical-tubular, bifid, with the teeth opposite. The flower long-stalked, erect. The [stamen] filaments alternate [with perianth-segments], the three alternate filaments are shorter, it seems to me. Commerson's specimens had no leaves.

3. AMARYLLIS *tubiflora*

    Native of Lima and Chancay [Pery] in sandy soils. [Specimen collected by Joseph] Dombey.

    Dombey says that the stamen filaments are equal, they seem to me to be subequal, but the specimen which I observed was hardly the best.

4. AMARYLLIS *spiralis*. Plate 13.

    Native of sandy soils, Cape Town, Cape of Good Hope. [Specimen collected by] Bruguière.

    The corolla is six-lobed, the limb is strongly spreading and [its lobes are] equal, the tube is short. The filaments are erect, the alternate ones are shorter. The scape is twisted at the base.

* * *[Species in which]* the limb of the corolla is bell-shaped *[and]* irregular,
the stamens declined*

5. AMARYLLIS *Atamasco* L.

Native of North America. Plant a perennial herb.

6. AMARYLLIS *maculata*

Native of Chile. [Specimen collected by Joseph] Dombey.

The scape [primary flower stalk] blotched by lines of dots. The corolla is bell-shaped.

[p. 11]   7. AMARYLLIS *chilensis*

Native of Chile. [Specimen collected by Joseph] Dombey.

The flowers purplish as in *A. Belladonna* or *reginae*.

8. AMARYLLIS *clavata*

Native of South Africa.

The flower is pedicelled [stalked].The [perianth-] tube is narrow, soon dilated at the base. The [perianth-] limb is very short.

I did not see the leaves, and I could not observe the stamens. It remains uncertain whether it belongs to this or the preceeding section [the two sections identified above by * and **].

9. AMARYLLIS *formosissima* L.

Native of Mexico. Plant a perennial herb.

It [the flower] simulates a polypetalous corolla [one composed of many distinct petals], but the petals are truly united at the base, the stamens are inserted in them as in the congeneric [species]: the three lower ones hang down. The throat is somewhat scaly.

10. AMARYLLIS *reginae*

[p. 12]   Native of Jamaica, Surinam. Plant a perennial herb.

11. AMARYLLIS *speciosa*

Native of South Africa. [Specimen collected by Francis] Masson.

This [species] is very close to the preceeding one. Is it distinct enough?

12. AMARYLLIS *reticulata*. Plate 14.

Native of Brazil?

It is distinguished by the petals, which are transversely veined.

The [perianth-] throat is smooth.

13. AMARYLLIS *Belladonna*

[p. 13]   Native on the promontory, Cape of Good Hope. Plant a perennial herb.

The [perianth-] segments alternately extrorsely and clearly recurved. The stigma divided into three parts.

14. AMARYLLIS *vittata*. Plate 15.

Place of nativity unknown. Plant a perennial herb.

The inner petals fused into a fleshy tube, but the margins of the outer ones are free to the base.

15. AMARYLLIS *falcata*
Native on the promontory at the Cape of Good Hope.

16. AMARYLLIS *longifolia* L.
Native on the promontory at the Cape of Good Hope.

17. AMARYLLIS *zeylanica* L.

[p. 14]   Native of the East Indies. Plant a perennial herb.

The fruit is viviparous [producing young plants while attached to flower stalk].

18. AMARYLLIS *revoluta*
Native on the promontory at the Cape of Good Hope.

19. AMARYLLIS *latifolia*
Native of the East Indies.
I did not see the plant.

20. AMARYLLIS *aurea*. Plate 15 *bis*.

Native of China. Plant a perennial herb.

The leaves are broadly linear, bright green. The scape is a foot high, 5-6-flowered. The flowers are short-stalked, tawny-yellow. The petals are narrow, those on the lower side separated and with wavy margins. The stigma is unlobed.

21. AMARYLLIS *orientalis* L.

[p. 15]   Native of the East Indies. Plant a perennial herb.

22. AMARYLLIS *ciliaris* L.

Native on the promontory at the Cape of Good Hope. Plant a perennial herb.

It remains uncertain whether this is an *Amaryllis* or rather is a *Haemanthus,* or whether there really are two [different kinds of] plants. I know of only one [specimen] namely Breyne's which was living but without flowers.

23. AMARYLLIS *umbella*. Plate 16.

Native on the promontory, at the Cape of Good Hope. [Specimen collected by Francis] Masson. Plant a perennial herb.

Flowers nodding. The corolla-tube top-shaped. The limb bell-shaped, erect.

24. AMARYLLIS *cylindracea*

Native on the promontory at the Cape of Good Hope. [Specimens collected by Francis] Masson, [and S.] Oldenburg.

* * * *[Species with] the corolla spreading radiately, the tube scarcely apparent [almost none]*

25. AMARYLLIS *sarniensis* L.

[p. 16]   Native of Japan. At Cape Town, Cape of Good Hope, [specimens collected by Francis] Masson [and S.] Oldenburg. Plant a perennial herb.

26. AMARYLLIS *radiata*

Place of nativity unknown. Plant a perennial herb.

27. AMARYLLIS *cinnamomea*. Plate 17.

Native on the promontory, Cape of Good Hope. [Specimen collected by Pierre] Bruguière.

Flowers are half as large as those in *A. undulata*. The petals are twice as broad, the outer margins strongly revolute. The stigma is unlobed. [The species is] related to *Haemanthus*.

28. AMARYLLIS *undulata*

Native on the promontory at the Cape of Good Hope. Plant a perennial herb.

The stigma is capitate [pin-headed]. The fruit is viviparous [cf. also no. 17].

[The species] *A. spiralis* [no. 4] could be placed here because of its very short [perianth-] tube equal [in size] to the wheel-shaped limb, but I have placed it in the first section because of the alternate shorter stamens.

Amaryllis capensis L. is *Hypoxis stellata* Linn. f. *Suppl.* p. 197.

—— *disticha* L. is an *Haemanthus?*

[p. 17]   AGAPANTHUS

AGAPANTHUS *umbellatus*

Native on the promontory at the Cape of Good Hope. Plant a perennial herb.

The flowers are definitely like those of *Hemerocallis*, but it is a distinct genus because of the spathe.

EUCOMIS

1. EUCOMIS *regia*

Native on the promontory at the Cape of Good Hope. Plant a perennial herb.

2. EUCOMIS *nana*

[p. 18]   Native on the promontory at the Cape of Good Hope. [Specimen collected by Francis] Masson. Plant a perennial herb.

Masson's specimen is one of foliage only. The leaves are ovate, [apices] acuminate, lined beneath; the veins meeting at the apex.

3. EUCOMIS *punctata*. Plate 18.

Native on the promontory at the Cape of Good Hope. Plant a perennial herb.

The coma [tuft of leaves above the flowers] is smaller and less dense than in the other species, the peduncles [meaning, pedicels] are longer and looser. *E. nana* is smaller [than] *E. regia,* [and] *E. punctata* is larger.

Plants with flowers having eight stamens

KOËLREUTERIA

KOËLREUTERIA *paullinioides*. Plate 19.
   Native of China. A woody plant.
   A tree producing polygamous flowers.

Plants with flowers having twenty or more stamens

EUCALYPTUS

EUCALYPTUS *obliqua*. Plate 20.
   Native of New South Wales. [Specimens collected by] Nelson [and] Wm. Anderson. A woody plant.

[p. 19]   *Plants with flowers having four stamens in two pairs, one pair longer than the other*

LAVANDULA

LAVANDULA *viridis*. Plate 21.
   Native of Madeira. [Specimen collected by Francis] Masson. A woody plant.
   It differs from *L. stoechas* by the leaves which are rugose [veins deeply impressed], villose [very long-hairy] and green, not grayish-downy [as is *L. stoechas*], the bracts and coma are entire and green, and not slightly 3-lobed and purplish.

BYSTROPOGON

1. BYSTROPOGON *pectinatum*
   Native of Peru. [Specimen collected by Joseph] Dombey, [and of] Jamaica.
2. BYSTROPOGON *sidaefolium*
   Native of Peru. [Specimen collected by Joseph] Dombey.
3. BYSTROPOGON *suaveolens*
[p. 20]   Native of North America.
4. BYSTROPOGON *plumosum*. Plate 22.
   Native of Tenerife, Canary Islands. [Specimen collected by Francis] Masson.

[The characteristics of] *B. plumosum* and *B. origanifolium* [nos. 4 and 5] connect *B. canariense* and *punctatum* [nos. 6 and 7] with those that precede [*i.e.*, with nos. 1-3].

5. BYSTROPOGON *origanifolium*

Native of Tenerife, Canary Islands. [Specimen collected by Francis] Masson. A woody plant.

[This species is] somewhat related to the preceding, but the leaves are wholly entire and whitish beneath.

6. BYSTROPOGON *canariense*

Native of the Madeira Islands, [and] Tenerife. [Specimen collected by Francis] Masson. A woody plant.

7. BYSTROPOGON *punctatum*. Plate 23.

Native of Madeira Islands. [Specimen collected by Joseph] Banks [and Daniel] Solander. A woody plant.

The calyx-teeth are not awl-shaped as in the others; nevertheless it is congeneric [with them].

[p. 21]

DIGITALIS

DIGITALIS *Sceptrum* L. Plate 24.

Native in shady woodlands of Madeira Islands. [Specimens collected by Francis] Masson. A woody plant.

CAPRARIA

CAPRARIA *undulata* L. Plate 24.

Native of the hills near [the village of] Swellendam [ca. 150 mi. north-east of] Cape of Good Hope. [Specimen collected by Francis] Masson. A woody plant.

Some of the leaves are almost whorled.

Plants with flowers having the stamens in two bundles

ASPALANTHUS

ASPALANTHUS *pedunculata*. Plate 26.

Native of the promontory, at the Cape of Good Hope. A woody plant.

*Plants with flowers having the stamen anthers fused to form a tube around the
style [Members of the family Compositae]*

TANACETUM

TANACETUM *flabelliforme*. Plate 27.

Native on promontory at the Cape of Good Hope. [Specimen collected by
Francis] Masson. Plant a perennial herb. [In this species] all of the florets are
bisexual [and the corrollas are] divided into five lobes, but because of the
naked receptacle, which is not chaffy, it [the species] belongs rather with
Tanacetum than with *Athanasia*.

[p. 22]

ARTEMISIA

ARTEMISIA argentea. Plate 28.

Native of the Madeira islands. [Specimen collected by Francis] Masson.
A woody plant.

[The plant] is wholly silvery. The receptacle [on which the flowers are
borne] is shaggy-hairy.

RELHANIA

[This genus] differs from *Athanasia* only by the ray-florets being unequal
[in size]. *Relhania* could thus be combined with Athanasia as a distinct section, a view supported by [the situation in] *Senecio* and other genera.
It is distinguished from *Leysera* by its membranous pappus which is not
plumose; from *Osmites* by the fertile female florets, and also by the scarious
calyx.

* [Species with] the flower [heads] aggregated

1. RELHANIA squarrosa. Plate 29.

   Native on the promontory of the Cape of Good Hope. [Specimen collected by Francis] Masson. A woody plant.

2. RELHANIA *genistifolia*.

   Native on the promontory of the Cape of Good Hope. [Specimens collected by Francis] Masson, [and Johann G.] Koenig. A woody plant.
3. RELHANIA *microphylla*.

   Native on the promontory of the Cape of Good Hope. [Specimen collected by Francis] Masson. A woody plant.

[p. 23]   4. RELHANIA *passerinoides*.

Native of Cape Town at the Cape of Good Hope. [Specimen collected by Francis] Masson. A woody plant.

The leaves and flowers [of this species] are twice as large as in *R. microphylla;* the stems are erect, not much branched.

5. RELHANIA *viscosa*

Native on the promontory at the Cape of Good Hope. [Specimen collected by Francis] Masson. A woody plant.

R. viscosa and *passerinoides* are somewhat similar in their inflorescence [characters] and in appearance, but in *R. viscosa* the leaves are somewhat 3-sided, slightly fleshy, [and are] sprinkled with stalked glands [pin-headed] which are lacking in *R. passerinoides*.

* * *[Species with] the flower [head] solitary*

6. RELHANIA *laxa*.

Native on the promontory at the Cape of Good Hope. [Specimen collected by Francis] Masson. Plant an annual herb.

7. RELHANIA *pedunculata*

Native on the promontory at the Cape of Good Hope.

8. RELHANIA *lateriflora*

Native on the promontory at the Cape of Good Hope. [Specimen collected by Francis] Masson.

9. RELHANIA *cuneata*

Native on the promontory at the Cape of Good Hope. [Specimen collected by Francis] Masson. A woody plant.

10. RELHANIA *virgata*

[p. 24]   Native on the promontory at the Cape of Good Hope. [Specimen collected by Francis] Masson. A woody plant.

[This species is] somewhat similar to the preceding, of which it is probably a variety.

11. RELHANIA *paleacea*

Native on the promontory at the Cape of Good Hope. [Specimen collected by Francis] Masson. A woody plant.

12. RELHANIA *santolinoides*

Native on the promontory at the Cape of Good Hope. [Specimen collected by Francis] Masson. A woody plant.

It is distinct enough from *R. paleacea?* In both [species] the pappus is tubular and toothed at the top.

13. RELHANIA *pungens*

Native on the promontory at the Cape of Good Hope. [Specimen collected by Francis] Masson. A woody plant.

14. RELHANIA *decussata*

Native on the promontory at the Cape of Good Hope. [Specimen collected by Francis] Masson. A woody plant.

15. RELHANIA *calycina*

Native on the promontory at the Cape of Good Hope. [Specimen collected by Francis] Masson. A woody plant.

In *R. pungens* the calyces are decussate [each pair at right angles to the adjoining pairs] showy, and are broader, the inner bracts are larger. This is scarcely so in *R. paleacea*.

16. RELHANIA *Bellidiastrum*

Native of Cape Town, at the Cape of Good Hope. [Specimen collected by Francis] Masson. A woody plant.

No pappus [is present. This species is] quite distinct from the genus [as a whole].

[p. 25]
CINERARIA

1. CINERARIA *humifusa*

Native on the promontory at the Cape of Good Hope. [Specimen collected by Francis] Masson. A woody plant.

[This species is] related to *C. cymbalarifolia,* but its florets are yellowish, the calyces [involucral bracts] are rough-hairy [villous-scabrous], while in *C. cymbalarifolia* the florets are purple and the calyces are smooth.

2. CINERARIA *viscosa*

Native on the promontory at the Cape of Good Hope. [This species] is probably only a variety of *C. humifusa.*

3. CINERARIA *scapiflora*

Native on the promontory at the Cape of Good Hope. [Specimen collected by Francis] Masson.

[In this species] the leaves are doubly-toothed or are somewhat lobed.

4. CINERARIA *mitellaefolia*

Native on the promontory at the Cape of Good Hope.

5. CINERARIA *lanata.* Plate 30.

Native of Tenerife, Canary Islands. A woody plant. The flowers are purple.

6. CINERARIA *populifolia*

[p. 26]
Native of the moist areas of the Canary Islands. [Specimen collected by Francis] Masson. A woody plant.

The flowers are yellow. The leaves resemble those of *Populus albus.*

7. CINERARIA *aurita.* Plate 31.

Native of the Madeira Islands. [Specimen collected by Francis] Masson. A woody plant.

The flowers are purple. The leaves are also poplar-like. It differs by having both larger and smaller auricles [at the base of the petioles].

8. CINERARIA *ramentosa*

Native of the Canary Islands. [Specimen collected by Francis] Masson. A woody plant.

The calyces [i.e., involucral bracts] have numerous minute scattered teeth [along the margins].

9. CINERARIA *malvaefolia*. Plate 32.

Native of the Canary Islands and of the island of St. Miguel of the Azores. [Specimen collected by Francis] Masson. A woody plant.

10. CINERARIA *multiflora*

Native of the hillsides of the Canary Islands. [Specimen collected by Francis] Masson.

11. CINERARIA *cruenta*. Plate 33.

Native of Tenerife, Canary Islands. [Specimen collected by Francis] Masson. A woody plant.

12. CINERARIA *tussilaginis*

Native of Tenerife, Canary Islands. [Specimen collected by Francis] Masson. Plant an annual herb.

13. CINERARIA *lobata*. Plate 34.

Native on the promontory, at the Cape of Good Hope. [Specimens collected by Sir Joseph] Banks and [Daniel] Solander, [and Francis] Masson. A woody plant.

[p. 27]   [This species] is scarcely distinguishable from *Senecio* by one or another bract under the calyces almost like a diminuitive calyx. It is an herb rather like *Cineraria*.

14. CINERARIA *senecionis*

Native on the promontory at the Cape of Good Hope. [Specimen collected by] Forster. A woody plant.

The cinerarias which have these diminuitive calyces, such as *C. americana* and *lineata,* should perhaps be placed more correctly in *Senecio*.

BOLTONIA

In Aster the calyx is imbricated [i.e., the involucral bracts are overlapping]. The pappus is pilose [soft-hairy]. The receptacle is naked according to Linnaeus, but actually is honeycombed [as described for the genus].

In *Matricaria* there is no pappus. The receptacle is naked.

In *Spilanthes* the corolla is more often uniform. The receptacle is chaffy.

1. BOLTONIA *glastifolia*. Plate 35. [Ed. note: this plate and the succeeding, although cited in the text, were never published.]

Native of North America. Plant a perennial herb.

2. BOLTONIA *asteroides.* Plate 36.

Native of the swamps of Virginia. [Specimen collected by] Bartram. Plant a perennial herb.

BUPHTHALMUM

BUPHTHALMUM *sericeum* L. Plate 37.

Native of Fuerteventura, Canary Islands. [Specimen collected by Francis] Masson. A woody plant.

STOKESIA

[p. 28]   [This genus is] related to *Carthamus,* from which it differs by the naked receptacle, the pappus of four filaments, and the florets rayed.

STOKESIA *cyanea.* Plate 38.

Native of South Carolina. Plant a perennial herb.

The corolla is like that of *Centaurea cyanus.* The calyx is almost that of *Carthamus.*

Plants with flowers having the stamens fused to the pistil [Orchids]

LIMODORUM

1. LIMODORUM *Tancarvilleae*

Native of China. Plant a perennial herb.

Although the nectary at the back of the labellum ends in a very short spur, there seems to be no reason for [this species] to be separated from *Limodorum.*

2. LIMODORUM *tuberosum* L.

Native of shady areas of Pennsylvania, [specimen collected by] Matthias Hultgren, [in] Maryland. Plant a perennial herb.

The racemes are simple [unbranched] in all of the specimens seen by me, and [as shown by] Miller, but Martyn depicts them as branched.

3. LIMODORUM *altum* L.

[Footnote below description:] Plumier's synonym must be excluded, since it shows a plant which has an unbranched raceme and not [one that is] paniculate, and since the flowers are clearly shown to be sessile.

Native of Jamaica. [Specimen collected by William] Houston. Plant a perennial herb.

Plants monoecious, the flowers unisexual and those of each sex on separate plants

GENESIPHYLLA

* *Flowers masculine [followed by description of same]*
** *The female flowers are intermixed with the male flowers among the same leaves at the apex*

If [this plant] cannot stand as a genus of its own, it should be joined with *Phyllanthus* rather than with *Xylophyllum*.

GENESIPHYLLA *asplenifolia*. Plate 39.
[Footnote below the synonyms:] The other synonyms [cited] by Linnaeus, namely those of Commelin, Plukenet, Catesby, Seba, as well as the *Phyllanthus* described by Browne as a perennial herb, and the *Phyllanthus epiphyllanthus* of Linnaeus, are to be reunited with *Xylophyllum falcatum* Swartz.
Native of Jamaica. Plant a perennial herb.

Plants dioecious, the flowers unisexual but those of both sexes on the same plant

TAMUS

TAMUS *elephantipes*. Plate 40.
Native on the promontory at the Cape of Good Hope. [Specimen collected by Francis] Masson. Plant a perennial herb.
Since plants bearing female flowers remain unknown, it is most difficult to decide with certainty between *Tamus* and *Smilax* [as to which is the correct genus for this specimen]. Nevertheless, a rudimentary ovary in the male [flower] with the style fused to the calyx indicates an inferior ovary, from which it is possible to deduce that it belongs in *Tamus*.

Plants having bisexual and unisexual flowers intermixed on the same individual

MIMOSA

1. MIMOSA *verticillata*. Plate 40.
Native of Tasmania. [Specimen collected by] Nelson. A woody plant.
2. MIMOSA *Houstoni*
Native of Vera Cruz, [Mexico. Specimen collected by William] Houston. A woody plant.
[In this species] the leaves are pilose [soft hairy] beneath. The inflores-

cences are as in *Mimosa grandiflora,* but the flowers are more minute. The corollas villose [shaggy-hairy] and persistent. The legumes [seed pods] are [shaped like] parallelograms, acuminate [at apices], and flat. [The sides of the pods] are bulged by the seeds, are somewhat downey, and reddish. The seeds are oblong, compressed, are marked on both sides by a band, are attached to both margins of the seam [with] those on one side alternating with those on the other side.

This is [the same species as] Linnaeus' *Gleditsia inermis.* More recent authors, such as Duhamel, Du Roi, and others, have taken it to be a spineless variety of *Gleditsia triacanthos,* instead of *Gleditsia inermis.*

3. MIMOSA *grandiflora.* Plate 42.

Native of the East Indies. A woody plant.

[This species] is very closely related to *Mimosa Houstoni,* from which it differs by the pinnules more dense, and the leaflets very distinctly ovate at the base, while in *M. Houstoni* those near the rachis [central leaf stalk] become confluent, are truncate at the base, and simulate a pinnatified leaf.

The cryptogamic [flowerless] plants. [Ferns only are treated here]

DICKSONIA

[p. 31]   1. DICKSONIA *arborescens.* Plate 43.

Native of the Island of St. Helena. [Specimen collected by Sir Joseph] Banks and [Daniel] Solander. A woody plant.

2. DICKSONIA *Culcita*

[Footnote to synonyms:] Concerning the Scythian Lamb, consult Deusing dissertation p. 598, Breyne's work cited above, and Kaempfer's *Amoenitatum exoticarum* p. 505 [1712]. If [the plant known as] Baromets and *Dicksonia Culcita* are not the same plant, which they probably are, even though their native lands are remote [from one another], without doubt [the plant known as] Agnus scythicus will be another species of fern.

The common name [for this species] in the Madeira Islands is *Feila Brom.*

Native of St. Miguel Island, Azores. [Specimen collected by Francis] Masson. Plant a perennial herb.

The inhabitants [of St. Miguel] make mattresses from the roots.

Additions and Corrections

Plants with bisexual flowers

EUCLEA

[p. 32]   There are flowers that are bisexual, [others that are] masculine-bisexual, namely with an abortive ovary from which it would appear as if polygamous. The female plant, if it exists, escapes me.

EUCLEA *racemosa* L.
   Native on the promontory, at the Cape of Good Hope. [Specimen collected by Francis] Masson. A woody plant.
   The capsules are definitely those of *Celastrus,* unless they are berried and horned, for which reason, the flower being unknown to me, I have placed them in this work as *Celastrus corniculatus.* The fruiting specimens of *Celastrus corniculatus* are as similar to *Euclea racemosa* as is one egg to another. Nevertheless I am surprised and you will scarcely believe that a two-ovaried plant like Euclea should enjoy a tri-locular fruit. Nor does the plant assigned to this genus by Thunberg with one-seeded berry bearing two styles make sense. Linnaeus calls the berry bilocular. Therefore this will have to be examined further by eyewitnesses.

[p. 33]   WITHERINGIA

Plants with flowers having four stamens and one ovary

   In memory of the celebrated William Withering, Doctor of Medicine, member of the Royal Society, London, author of the work entitled: *Botanical arrangements of British Plants.*

WITHERINGIA *solanacea*
   Native of Central America. Plant a perennial herb.

Explanation of the Plate

   The habit of the plant shown natural size [in the original volume, × 2/3 in the facsimile reproduction].

1. Flower, front view
2. ———, back view
3. Corolla, viewed from lower side
4. ———, expanded to show stamens and nectaries   } about natural size
5. Stamen
6. Pistil

[p. 34] The place of nativity [for this species] is reported to be Central America. It was first flowered [in Britain] by Robert James Petre, an English peer. [Robert James, the 8th Baron Petre [1713-42] was succeeded by Robert Edward [1742-87?] and who is probably meant here.] Today it grows in the garden at Kew. It flowers each year in the summer, but up to now it has not produced any fruit. Until now it seems to be propagated by root cuttings from the parent plant. It is cultivated in a "Cape House" [stove, or cool conservatory].

Distinguishing Characteristics

Witheringia differs from *Solanum* by the number of its [floral] parts, by the imperforate anthers [dehiscing by slits rather than by pores], and by the nectary: it differs from *Atropa* by the [floral] parts in fours, and by the nectary: it differs from *Aquartia* [a Jacquin genus now included in *Solanum*] by the equal calyx not having the alternate lobes 2-3 times as large, by the corolla-limb [lobes] being lanceolate and not linear and very long, by the anthers laterally dehiscent, not perforated at the top, and also by the nectary.

[p. 35] # CHLORANTHUS

[Synonym =] the genus *Nigrina* of Thunberg. Plants with flowers having four stamens and one ovary.

Olof Swartz said that the name Chloranthus came from the Greek ΧΛΩΡΟΣ [chloros] meaning green, and ΑΝΘΟΣ [anthos] meaning flower, because its flowers have the color of grass.

CHLORANTHUS *inconspicuus*
Native of China. A woody plant.

Explanation of the Plate
[See Plate 2]

The habit of the plant shown natural size.
1. Section of the spicate inflorescence (enlarged at right).
2. Flower, interior side view.

[xc]

3. ———, exterior side view.

4. Petals, interior top view [actually, flower of no. 2 with pistil removed].

5. ———, exterior side view [pedicel removed].

6. Pistil, front view.

7. ———, side view.

8. Fruit, side view.

9. ———, front view.

10. Seed.

[Nos. 1-7, and 9, larger than natural size, nos. 8 and 10 nearly natural size.]

[p. 36]   [Footnote to pericarp description:] The perianth proper [of the flower] and the scar of the fallen petal [i.e., of the corolla] gradually rise as the fruit matures, until the berries are on top, and from this it can be assumed that the ovary is truly inferior, even though it would rather seem to be superior.

A living specimen [of this species] was brought to England from China by James Lind, D.M. in 1781. It blossomed while the ship Atlas was delivering it. I took care to sketch [or describe] it while it blossomed in the nursery of James Lee, and I observed it bearing fruit shortly afterwards at the Royal Gardens, Kew. It blossoms very often [during] the same year and produces very little fruit. It is grown in a warm conservatory. It is propagated by suckers and stolons.

Doctor Lind reported that it was mixed by the Chinese with leaves of tea, and that the tea then gave off a sweet fragrance, but that the *Chloranthus* itself is without fragrance. It is as yet unknown for what use the Chinese cultivate this relatively unattractive plant, which I have seen in many collections of Chinese illustrations of garden plants.

Explanation of Abbreviations

Act. holm. ~ Kongliga Svenska Vetenskaps-akademien, Handlingar. Vol. 3, 1742. [*cf.* Anmärkningar öfwer Amaryllis den sköna, af Carl Linnaeus, pp. 93-102, plate 6.]

A. DC. ~ CANDOLLE, Alphonse de [1806-1893].

Ait., Hort. Kew. ~ AITON, William [1731-1793]. Hortus Kewensis. London, 1789. (Pritzel 78)

Ald. farn. ~ ALDINUS, Tobias [17th Cent.]. Exactissima descriptio rariorum quarundam plantarum qua continentur Rome in horto Farnesiano. Rome, 1625. (Pritzel 1590)

Alg. Konst Letter-bode ~ Algemeene Konst- Letter-bode [Haarlem,] 1788-1862.

Allg. Litt. Zeit. ~ Allgemeine Literatur-Zeitung. [Halle, Jena,] 1785-1849.

Ann. Bot. Konig & Sims. ~ Annals of Botany [ed. by Charles Konig and John Sims]. London, 1805-06.

Ann. Bot. Usteri. ~ Annalen der Botanik [ed. by Paul Usteri]. Zürich, 1791-93, continued as "Neue Annalen…"

Ann. Mus. Nat. Hist. ~ Annales, Muséum (National) d'Histoire naturelle, Paris, 1802-13.

Ann. Sc. Nat. Bot. ser. ~ Annales des Sciences Naturelles, Botanique, series…, Paris, 1834+

Anon. ~ Anonymous, no author's name cited in the work.

Apr. ~ April.

Barrel. ic. ~ BARRELIER, Jacques [1606-1673]. Icones plantarum per Galliam, Hispaniam, et Italiam observatarum ad vivam exhibitarum. [334 pls.]. Paris, 1714. (Pritzel 423)

Barrel. rar. ~ BARRELIER, Jacques. Plantae per Galliam, Hispaniam et Italiam observatae [Text, pp. 4, xxvi, 8, 8, 140]. Paris, 1714. (Pritzel 423)

Bauh. hist. ~ BAUHIN, Johann [1541-1613] & CHERLER, Johann Heinrich [1570-1610]. Historia plantarum universalis. 3 vols. Yverdun, 1650-51. (Pritzel 504)

Bauh. pin. ~ BAUHIN, Caspar [1560-1624]. [Pinax] theatri botanici. Basel, 1623. (Pritzel 509) (1671 ed.)

Benth. ~ BENTHAM, George [1800-1884].

Berg. cap. ~ BERGIUS, Peter Jonas [1730-1790]. Descriptiones plantarum ex Capite Bonae Spei. Stockholm, 1767. (Pritzel 673)

Biogr. Univ. (Michaud). ~ Biographie Universelle (ed. by Joseph-François Michaud). Paris, 1811-28; ed. 2, 1843-65.

BM ~ British Museum (Natural History), London, herbarium of.

Bot. Mag. ~ Curtis's Botanical Magazine containing coloured figures… of choice plants. London, 1787+

Bot. Reg. ~ The Botanical Register: consisting of coloured figures of exotic plants… by Sydenham Edwards. London, 1815-27. [Continued by John Lindley as Edward's Botanical Register 1828-47.]

Breyn. act. angl. ~ Breyne in The Royal Society, Philosophical Transactions, no. 390, 1725. [*i.e.,* Acta Anglica]

Breyn. cent. ~ BREYNE, Jakob [1637-1697]. Exoticarum aliarumque minus cognitarum plantarum centuria prima. Danzig, 1678. (Pritzel 1136)

Breyn. ic. and *Breyn. icon.* ~ BREYNE, Jakob. Icones rariorum et exoticarum plantarum. In Prodromi fasciculi rariorum plantarum primus et secundus. Danzig, 1739. (Pritzel 1139)

Breyn. prod. ~ BREYNE, Jakob. Prodromus fasciculi rariorum plantarum secundus… Danzig, 1689. (Pritzel 1138)

Briq. ~ BRIQUET, John Isaac [1870-1931].

Brongn. ~ BRONGNIART, Adolphe Théodore [1801-1876].

Brown. jam. ~ BROWNE, Patrick [1720-1790]. The civil and natural history of Jamaica. London, 1756. (Pritzel 1253)

Burm. afr. ~ BURMAN, Johannes [1706-1779]. Rariorum africanarum plantarum … decas prima [-decima]. Amsterdam, 1738-39. (Pritzel 1390) or Catalogi duo plantarum africanarum… Amsterdam, 1737. (Pritzel 1389)

Burm. f. ~ BURMAN, Nikolaus Laurens, *filius* [1734-1793].

Burm. prodr. ∼ BURMAN, Nikolaus Laurens [1734-1793]. Prodromus florae Capensis. In Flora Indica. Leyden, 1768. (Pritzel 1396)

ca. ∼ circa (Latin, about).

Catesb. car. ∼ CATESBY, Mark [1680-1749]. The natural history of Carolina, Florida and the Bahama Islands. 2 vols. London, 1731-1743. (Pritzel 1602)

cf. ∼ conferus (Latin, see ...).

CGE ∼ University of Cambridge, England, Botany School, herbarium of.

Char. gen. ∼ Forster, Johann Reinhold [1729-1798] & Johan Georg Adam [1754-1794]. Characteres generum plantarum ... Londini, 1776. (Pritzel 2981)

Clayt. virg. ∼ GRONOVIUS, Johannes Fridericus [1690-1762]. Flora Virginica exhibens plantas quas ... Claytonius in Virginia crescentes observavit ... Leyden, 1739. (Pritzel 3607)

Clus. hist. ∼ CLUSIUS, Carolus [1525-1609]. Rariorum plantarum historia. Antwerp, 1601. (Pritzel 1759)

cm. ∼ Centimeter.

comm. ∼ communicavit (Latin, has informed).

Comm. hort. ∼ COMMELIN, Jan. [1629-1692]. Horti medici Amstelodamensis rariorum ... plantarum ... descriptio et icones ... 2 vols. Amsterdam, 1697, 1701. (Pritzel 1833)

Comm. rar. ∼ COMMELIN, Caspar [1667-1731]. Horti medici Amstelaedamensis plantae rariores ... Leyden, 1706. (Pritzel 1837)

Corn. can. ∼ CORNUTI, Jacques Philippe [1606-1651]. Canadensium plantarum ... historia. Paris, 1635. (Pritzel 1894)

corr. ∼ correspondence.

D. ∼ Dominus (Latin honorific, sometimes meaning Mister).

Dalech. hist. ∼ DALECHAMPS, Jacques [1513-1588]. Historia generalis plantarum. Lyons, 1587, 1586. (Pritzel 2035)

DC. ∼ CANDOLLE, Auguste Pyramus DE [1778-1841].

D.C. ∼ District of Columbia (U.S.A.).

Dec. ∼ December.

Del. opusc. bot. ∼ USTERI, Paul [1768-1831]. Delectus opusculorum botanicorum, ... 2 vols. Argentoriati 1790-93. (Pritzel 9647)

Delarb. ∼ DELARBRE, Antoine [1724-1841].

Deusing. diss. ∼ DEUSING, Anton [1612-1666]. Dissertationes de Manna et Saccharo. Groningen, 1659. (Pritzel 2215)

Dict. Nat. Biogr. ∼ The Dictionary of National Biography. London, 21 vols. 1885-90; vols. 22-26, 1890-91; vols. 27-66, 1891-1901.

Dill. elth. ∼ DILLENIUS, Johann Jakob [1687-1747]. Hortus Elthamensis. London, 1732. (Pritzel 2285)

Dod. pempt. ∼ DODOENS, Rembert [1517-1585]. Stirpium historiae pemptades sex. Antwerp, 1583. (Pritzel 2350)

Dur. burg. ∼ DURANDE, Jean François [1730-1794]. Flore de Bourgogne. Dijon, 1782. (Pritzel 2551)

Duret, hist. ∼ DURET, Claude [?-1611]. Histoire admirable des plantes et herbes ... Paris, 1605. (Pritzel 2553)

Eckl. ∼ ECKLON, Christian Frederik [1795-1868].

ed(s). ∼ edition(s), editor.

e.g. ∼ exempli gratia (Latin, for example).

Ehret. pict. ∼ EHRET, Georg Dionysius [1708-1770]. Plantae et papiliones rariores depictae et aeri incisae. London, 1748-59. (Pritzel 2641)

Enum. Pl. Carib. ∼ JACQUIN, Nicolaus Joseph [1727-1817]. Enumeratio systematica plantarum, quas in insulis Caribaeis ... detectus novas ... Lugduni Batavorum, 1760. (Pritzel 4360)

etc. ∼ et cetera (Latin, and so forth).

Feb. ∼ February.

Fern. ∼ FERNALD, Merritt Lyndon [1837-1950].

Ferr. flor. ∼ FERRARI, Giovanni Battista [1584-1655]. De florum cultura libri IV ... Rome, 1633. (Pritzel 2877)

Feuill. mss. ~ An unpublished manuscript by Feuillée, probably in Paris.

Feuill. obs. ~ FEUILLÉE, Louis [1660-1732]. Journal des observations physiques, mathématiques et botaniques ... Paris, 1714. (Pritzel 2882)

Field Mus. Bot. ~ Field Museum of Natural History, Botanical series. Chicago, 1895+

Fisch. ~ FISCHER, Friedrich Ernst Ludwig von (1782-1854).

Fl. Cap. ~ HARVEY, William Henry [1811-1866] & SONDER, Otto Wilhelm [1812-1888]. Flora Capensis. 7 vols. Dublin, 1859-65; London, 1896-1933.

Fl. Cap. Penin. ~ ADAMSON, Robert S. [1885-] & SALTER, T. M. Flora of the Cape Peninsula. Cape Town, S. A., 1950.

fo. ~ folio.

G ~ Conservatoire et Jardin botaniques, Geneva, herbarium of.

Germ. em. ~ GERARD, John [1545-1607]. The herball, or General historie of plantes, ... enlarged and amended by Thomas Johnson. London, 1633 [ed. of 1636 is a reprint]. (Pritzel 3282)

GOET ~ Göttingen Universität, Systematisch-geobotanisches Institut, herbarium of.

Gott. Gelehrte Anz. ~ Göttingische Anzeigen von gelehrten Sachen [Königliche Gesellschaft der Wissenschaften]. Göttingen, 1753-1823.

Haller hist. ~ HALLER, Albert von [1708-1777]. Historia stirpium indigenarum Helvetiae inchoata. 3 vols. Berne, 1768. (Pritzel 3725)

Harv. ~ HARVEY, William Henry [1811-1866].

Heist. monogr. ~ HEISTER, Lorenz [1683-1758]. Descriptio novi generis plantae ex bulbosarum classe, cui Brunsvigiae nomen imposuit. Brunswick, 1753. (Pritzel 3922)

Herb. ~ HERBERT, William [1778-1847].

herb. spec. ~ herbarium specimen(s).

Herm. Lugd. b. ~ HERMANN, Paul [1640-1695]. Horti academici Lugduno Batavi catalogus ... Leyden, 1687. (Pritzel 3991)

Herm. par. ~ HERMANN, Paul. Paradisus Batavus ... cui accessit catalogus plantarum ... Leyden, 1698. (Pritzel 3994)

Hill, kew. ~ HILL, John [ca. 1716-1775]. Hortus Kewensis; ... London, 1768; [ed. 2] 1769. (Pritzel 4069)

Hoffmgg. ~ HOFFMANNSEGG, Johann Centurius von [1766-1849].

Hook. f. ~ HOOKER, Joseph Dalton, *filius* [1817-1911].

Hort. ~ hortus (Latin, garden; often used to indicate "of garden origin")

Hort. Brit. ~ LOUDON, John Claudius [1783-1843]. Hortus Britannicus ... 2 vols. 1830. (Pritzel 5627)

Hort. Kew ~ Royal Botanic Garden, Kew.

Hort. Kew. (also *Hort. kew.*) ~ AITON, William [1731-1793]. Hortus Kewensis. London, 1789. (Pritzel 78)

Hort. Reg. ~ Hortus Regius (Jardin du Roi, Paris).

Houst. mss. ~ HOUSTON, William [1695?-1733]. Reliquiae Houstounianae [Interleaved, annotated copy, with mss. identifications, at Library of the Linnean Society of London.] London, 1781.

Houst. rel. ~ HOUSTON, William. Reliquiae Houstounianae London, 1781. (Pritzel 4290)

Houtt. nat. hist. ~ HOUTTUYN, Martin [1720-1798]. Natuurlijke historie. Amsterdam, 1761-85. (Pritzel 5404)

hybrid. nov. ~ hybrida nova (Latin, new hybrid).

i.e. ~ id est (Latin, that is).

Jacq. amer. ~ JACQUIN, Nicolaus Joseph [1727-1817]. Selectarum stirpium americanarum historia ... Vienna, 1763; [ed. 2] Mannheim, 1788. (Pritzel 4362)

Jacq. hort. ~ JACQUIN, Nicolaus Joseph. Hortus botanicus Vindobonensis. 3 vols. Vienna, 1770-76. (Pritzel 4365)

Jan. ~ January.

Je. ~ June.

J. F. Mill. ic. ~ MILLER, John Frederick [ca. 1750-ca. 1794]. Icones animalium et plantarum, [London], 1776-94. (Pritzel 6233)

J. Hill. ~ HILL, John [ca. 1716-1775].

J. Sm. ~ SMITH, James Edward [1759-1828].

Journ. Bot. ~ Journal of Botany, British and Foreign, London, 1863-1942.

Journ. Bot. Schrad. ~ Journal für die Botanik (ed. by Heinrich Adolph Schrader). Göttingen, 1799-[1803].

Journ. S. Afr. Bot. ~ Journal of South African Botany. Cape Town, S. A., 1935+

K ~ The Royal Botanic Gardens, Kew, England, herbarium of.

Kaempf. amoen. ~ KAEMPFER, Engelbert [1651-1716]. Amoenitatum exoticarum politico-physico-medicarum fasciculi V. Lemgo, 1712. (Pritzel 4564)

L ~ Leiden, Netherlands, Rijksherbarium.

L. ~ LINNAEUS, Carl [1707-1778].

Lam. ~ LAMARCK, Jean Baptiste Antoine Pierre Monnet de [1744-1829].

Laxm. nov. comm. petr. ~ LAXMANN, Eric [1737-1796]. In, Academia Scientiarum Imperialis Petropolitana, Novi Commentarii [Vol. 17, 1772].

Less. ~ LESSING, Christian Friedrich [1810-1862].

L. f. ~ LINNAEUS, Carl, *filius* [1741-1783].

L'Hérit. ~ L'HÉRITIER DE BRUTELLE, Charles Louis [1746-1800]. *(Cf.* also Sert. Angl.)

Licet. spont. ~ LICETUS, Fortunius [1577-1657]. De spontaneo viventium ortu. Libri 4, p. 323, Vicetiae, 1618.

LINN ~ Linnaeus, a designator for the herbaria of Carl Linnaeus, and of his son Carl *filius*, at the Linnean Society (London).

Linn. amoen. ~ LINNAEUS, Carl [1707-1778]. Amoenitates academicae, seu dissertationes variae ... 7 vols. Stockholm and Leipzig, 1749-79. (Pritzel 5425)

Linn. cliff. ~ LINNAEUS, Carl. Hortus Cliffortianus. Amsterdam, 1737 [1738]. (Pritzel 5408)

Linn. f. Suppl. ~ LINNAEUS, Carl, filius. Supplementum plantarum systematis vegetabilium, ... Brunswick 1781. (Pritzel 5430)

Linn. mant. ~ LINNAEUS, Carl. Mantissa plantarum. Stockholm, 1767. (Pritzel 5429).

Linn. Soc. ~ The Linnean Society (London). [*Linn. Soc. Smith. Mss.* = Linnean Society collection of letters and papers of J. E. Smith.]

Linn. spec. ~ LINNAEUS, Carl. Species plantarum. Ed. 2, 2 vols. Stockholm, Wien, 1762-63. (Pritzel 5427)

Linn. Suppl. ~ see Linn. f. Suppl.

Linn. syst. ~ LINNAEUS, Carl. Systema naturae. Ed. 12, [vol. 2]. Stockholm, 1767. (Pritzel 5404)

Linn. ups. ~ LINNAEUS, Carl. Hortus Upsaliensis. Vol. I. Stockholm, 1748. (Pritzel 5423)

Linn. vir. ~ LINNAEUS, Carl. Viridarium Cliffortianum. Amsterdam, 1737. (Pritzel 5409)

Linn. zeyl. ~ LINNAEUS, Carl. Flora Zeylanica. Stockholm, 1747. (Pritzel 5422)

Lob. ic. ~ LOBEL, Matthias [1538-1616]. Plantarum seu stirpium icones. Antwerp, 1581. (Pritzel 5549)

Loud. Hort. Brit. ~ LOUDON, John Claudius [1783-1843]. Hortus Britannicus ... 2 vols. London, 1830. (Pritzel 5627)

L. Sp. pl. ~ LINNAEUS, Carl. Species plantarum. 2 vols. Holmiae, 1753.

LT ~ Lectotype. An herbarium specimen selected and designated as the nomenclatural type for the plant cited.

M. ~ Monsieur.

Mag. Bot. Roemer et Usteri. ~ Magazin für die Botanik ... [ed. by Johann Jacob Roemer and Paul Usteri]. Zürich, 1787-1790. (Pritzel 7706)

Mag. Enc. ~ Magasin encyclopédique. Paris, 1795-1816.

Mak. ~ MAKINO, Tomitaro [1863-1956].

Mart. cent. ~ MARTYN, John [1699-1768]. Historiae plantarum rariorum centuriae primae decas I-V ... London, 1728. (Pritzel 5921)

Masf. ~ MASFERRER Y ARQUIMBAU, Ramón [1849-1899].

Mass. ~ Massachusetts.

Med.-chir. Zeit. Salzburg. ~ Medicinisch-chirurgische Zeitung. Salzburg, 1790-1839.

Meerb. icon. ~ MEERBURGH, Nicolaas [1734-1814]. Afbeeldingen van zeldsaame gewassen. Leyden, 1775. (Pritzel 6044)

Mem. Inst. Nat. Sc. Arts. Cl. Sc. Math. Phys. ~ Mémoires de l'Institut national des Sciences et Arts, Classe des Sciences Mathématiques et Physiques. Paris, 1796-1804.

Mer. sur. ~ MERIAN, Maria Sybilla [1647-1717]. Dissertatio de generatione et metamorphosibus insectorum Surinamensium. Amsterdam, 1705. (Pritzel 6105)

Mill. dict. ~ MILLER, Philip [1691-1771]. The gardeners dictionary, ... Ed. 8, London, 1768. (Pritzel 6237)
Mill ic. ⎱ MILLER, Philip. Figures of the most beautiful, useful, and uncommon plants described
Mill icon. ⎰ in the Gardeners Dictionary ... 2 vols. London [1755-] 1760. (Pritzel 6241)

Mill. illust. ~ MUELLER, Johann Sebastian [1715-ca. 1790]. Illustratio systematis sexualis Linnaei. London, 1777. (Pritzel 6523)

Milne-Redh. ~ MILNE-REDHEAD, Edgar Wolston Bertram Handsley, [1906-].

Mme. ~ Madame.

MO ~ Missouri Botanical Garden, St. Louis, Mo., herbarium of.

Monthly Rev. London. ~ Monthly Review, London, [1749-1844]. [Title and subtitle varies.]

Mor. hist. ~ MORISON, Robert [1620-1683]. Plantarum historia universalis Oxoniensis. 2 vols. Oxford, 1680-99. (Pritzel 6464)

MPU ~ Institute Botanique, Université de Montpellier, herbarium of.

Mss. ~ Manuscripts.

Muell. ~ MUELLER, Johann Sebastian (later changed to John Miller). [1715-ca. 1790].

Murr. syst. ~ MURRAY, Johann Anders [1740-1791]. C. a Linné ... systema vegetabilium ... editio decima tertia ... adornata a J. A. Murray. Göttingen & Gotha, 1774. (Pritzel 5430)

no. ~ numero (Latin, number).

nom. illegit. ~ nomen illegitimum (a Latin name which, for nomenclatural reasons, is illegitimate and without any standing in botanical nomenclature; an incorrect name).

Nouv. Biogr. Gén. ~ Nouvelle Biographie Générale. 46 vols. Paris, 1852-1866.

Nov. ~ November.

Novi Comm. Acad. Sc. Petropol. ~ Novi Commentarii Academiae Scientiarum Imperialis Petropolitanae [St. Petersburg] 1747-75. [Often listed now under Akademiia nauk S.S.S.R., Leningrad.]

NY ~ New York Botanical Garden, herbarium of.

Obs. Phys. Hist. Arts. ~ Observations sur la Physique, sur l'Histoire naturelle et sur les Arts et Métiers. Paris, 1773-1793.

O. Ktze. ~ KUNTZE, Otto [1843-1907].

orig. ~ Original.

OXF ~ Oxford University, England, Fielding and Druce Herbaria.

P ~ Muséum National d'Histoire naturelle. Paris, herbarium of.

p., pp. ~ page, pages.

Park. theat. ~ PARKINSON, John [1567-1650]. Theatrum botanicum ... or An herball ... London, 1640. (Pritzel 6934)

Pav. ~ PAVÓN, José [1754-1844].

Pet. gaz. ~ PETIVER, James [1663-1718]. Gazophylacii naturae et artis decades X. 2 vols. London, 1702-09. (Pritzel 7088)

Philos. Trans. Roy. Soc. ~ Philosophical Transactions of the Royal Society of London, 1665+

Plukn. almag. ~ PLUKENET, Leonard [1642-1706]. Almagestum botanicum ... London, 1696. (Pritzel 7212)
Plukn. amalth. ~ PLUKENET, Leonard. Amaltheum botanicum. London, 1705. (Pritzel 7212)

Plum. cat. ~ PLUMIER, Charles [1646-1704]. Catalogus plantarum Americanarum. [In his Nova plantarum Americanarum genera.] Paris, 1703. (Pritzel 7214)

Poit. ~ POITEAU, Antoine [1766-1854].

Port. phyt. ~ PORTA, Giambattista [1538-1615]. Phytognomica octo libris contenta. [Liber IIII, Cap. IIII cf. p. 162] Naples, 1588. (Pritzel 7273)

Presl. ~ PRESL, Karel Boriwog [1794-1852].

Prod. Herb. ~ Prodromus Herbarium, the herbarium of De Candolle at Geneva, on which was based his *Prodromus*.

publ. ~ published.

Putterl. ~ PUTTERLICK, Aloys [1810-1845].

Rai. hist. ~ RAY, John [1628-1705]. Historia plantarum. 3 vols. London, 1686-1704. (Pritzel 7436)

R. Br. ~ BROWN, Robert [1773-1855].

repr. ~ reprinted.

Rev. ~ Reverend.

rev. ~ revised.

Rev. Biblioth. ~ Revue des Bibliothèques. Paris, 1891-1936.

Rheed. mal. ~ RHEEDE TOT DRAAKESTEIN, Hendrik Adriaan van [1635-1691]. Hortus Indicus Malabaricus. 12 vols. Amsterdam, 1678-1703. (Pritzel 7585)

R. H. S. Dict. Gard. ~ The Royal Horticultural Society Dictionary of Gardening. (Ed. by Fred J. Chittenden). 4 vols. Oxford, 1951. Ed. 2, 1956.

Roy. Bot. Gard. Kew. ~ Royal Botanic Gardens, Kew. Richmond, Surrey, England.

Rudb. elys. ~ RUDBECK, Olof [1630-1702]. Campi Elysii liber primus ... 2 vols. Upsala, 1701-02. (Pritzel 7860, 7861)

Rumph. ⎫ ~ RUMPF, Georg Eberhard [1627-1702]. Herbarium Amboinense ... Amsterdam, 1750.
Rumph. amb. ⎭   (Pritzel 7908)

s ~ Naturhistoriska Riksmuseum, Botanical Department, Stockholm.

Salisb. ~ SALISBURY, Richard Anthony [1761-1829].

SBT ~ Hortus Botanicus Bergianus, Stockholm.

Scal. subt. exerc. ~ SCALIGER, Julius Caesar [1484-1558]. Exotericarum exercitationum liber quintus decimus de subtilitate ad Hieronymum Cardanum. Lutetiae [Paris]. 1557. (Pritzel 8089)

Schultz Bip. ~ SCHULTZ, Carl Heinrich, "Bipontinus" (of Zweibrücken) [1805-1867].

Schweick. ~ SCHWEICKERDT, Herold Georg Wilhelm Johannes [1903-].

S. C. ~ South Carolina.

Scopoli carn. ~ SCOPOLI, Giovanni Antonio [1723-1788]. Flora Carniolica. Vienna, 1760. (Pritzel 8553)

s.d. ~ sine dato (Latin, without date).

Seb. thes. ~ SEBA, Albertus [1665-1736]. Locupletissimi rerum naturalium thesauri accurata descriptio ... 4 vols. Amsterdam, 1734-65. (Pritzel 8562)

sem. ~ semester

sep. ~ September

Sert. Angl. ~ L'HÉRITIER DE BRUTELLE, Charles Louis [1746-1800]. Sertum Anglicum. Paris 1788 [1789-1792]. (Pritzel 5270)

s.l. ~ sine loco (Latin, without place [of publication]).

Sloan. act. angl. ~ SLOANE, Sir Hans in The Royal Society, Transactions. Vol. 20, no. 246, 1698.

Sloan. cat. ~ SLOANE, Sir Hans [1660-1753]. Catalogus plantarum quae in insula Jamaica sponte proveniunt vel vulgo coluntur. London, 1696. (Pritzel 8722)

Sloan. hist. ~ SLOANE, Sir Hans. A voyage to the Island Madera, Barbados ... and Jamaica, with the natural history ... 2 vols. London, 1707-25. (Pritzel 8723)

Sloan. jam. ~ SLOANE, Sir Hans. Catalogus plantarum quae in insula Jamaica sponte proveniunt vel vulgo coluntur. London, 1696. (Pritzel 8722)

Solan. tab. ~ Solana tabulae [with reference to L'Héritier's plates of *Solanum* species].

Sond. ~ SONDER, Otto Wilhelm [1812-1888].

sp. nov. ~ species nova.

Sp. Pl. ~ LINNAEUS, Carl (1707-1778). Species plantarum, ed. 1, Holmiae 1753; ed. 2, Holmiae, 1763.

Spreng. ~ SPRENGEL, Kurt [1766-1833].

Steud. ~ STEUDEL, Ernst Gottlieb [1783-1856].

Suppl. ~ Supplement [*cf.* also *Linn. f. Suppl.*].

Swartz. act. lond. ~ SWARTZ, Olof, In the Royal Society, Philosophical Transactions, vol. 78, 1787.

Swert, flor.) ~ SWEERTS, Emanuel. Florilegium ... ad vivum dilineatum Frankfurt, 1612. Amster-
Swertz. flor.)   dam, 1620. (Pritzel 9073)

Sw. ~ SWARTZ, Olof Peter [1760-1818].

Syst. ~ LINNAEUS, Carl [1707-1778] Systema vegetabilium ... Ed. 13 (ed. by Johann Andreas Murray).
  Göttingen, 1774.

T ~ Type. An herbarium specimen of the plant on which the author of the name in question
  based that name.

t. ~ tabula (Latin, for plate, usually for a full-page illustration).

Tab. ic. ~ TABERNAEMONTANUS, Jacobus & Theodorus aus Bergzabern [*ca.* 1520-1590]. Eicones plantarum ... Francofurti ad Moenum, 1590. (Pritzel 9094)

Thell. ~ THELLUNG, Albert [1881-1928].

Thunb. gen. ~ THUNBERG, Carl Pehr [1743-1822]. Nova genera plantarum. Praeses C. P. Thunberg, etc.
  Upsala, [1781-1801]. (Pritzel 9266)

Thunb. jap. ~ THUNBERG, Carl Pehr. Flora Japonica. Leipzig, 1784. (Pritzel 9257)

Tourn. inst. ~ TOURNEFORT, Joseph Pitton de [1656-1708]. Institutiones rei herbariae; editio altera
  (ed. 2). 3 vols. Paris, 1700. (Pritzel 9427)

Trans. Linn. Soc. ~ Transactions of the Linnean Society, London, 1791-1875.

Trew. comm. litter. anno 1744 ~ TREW, Christoph Jakob, communicated in a letter of the year 1744.

Trew. ehret. ~ TREW, Christoph Jakob [1695-1769]. Plantae selectae, quarum imagines pinxit ... Ehret.
  Nuremberg, 1750-73. (Pritzel 9499)

Trew, seligm. ~ TREW, Christoph Jakob. Hortus nitidissimis ... superbiens floribus. Ed. Seligmann.
  3 vols. Nürnberg, 1750-86. (Pritzel 9500)

tt. ~ tabulae. (Plural of tabula (t.), which see.)

Turcz. ~ TURCZANINOW, Nicolai Stepanowich [1796-1864].

UPS ~ Institute of Systematic Botany, Botanical Garden and Botanical Museum of the University
  of Uppsala.

Vaill. act. par. 1724 ~ VAILLANT, Sébastien [1669-1722]. In [Paris] Académie Royale des Sciences, Mémoires. 1724.

vo. ~ verso (Latin, for the left-hand, even-numbered, page of a book).

Weinm. phyt. ~ WEINMANN, Johann Wilhelm [1683-1741]. Phytanthoza iconographia. 4 vols. Regens-
  burg, 1737-45. (Pritzel 10140)

Willd. ~ WILLDENOW, Carl Ludwig von [1765-1812].

SERTUM ANGLICUM

FACSIMILE

Car. Lud. L'HÉRITIER, Dom. *de Brutelle*,

in Aulâ Juvam. Par. Reg. Consil.

SERTUM ANGLICUM,

SEU

PLANTÆ RARIORES

QUÆ IN HORTIS JUXTA LONDINUM,

IMPRIMIS

IN HORTO REGIO KEWENSI

EXCOLUNTUR

Ab anno 1786 ad annum 1787 observatæ.

———

PARISIIS,

TYPIS PETRI-FRANCISCI DIDOT.

Prostat ⎰ PARISIIS, apud ⎱ LUD. NIC. PRÉVOST.
⎰ ⎱ THEOPHIL. BARROIS.
LONDINI, apud PETR. ELMSLY.
VIENNÆ et LIPSIÆ, apud RUD. GRÆFFER.
ARGENTORATI, apud AMAND. KOENIG.

——

1788.

LECTORI BOTANICO S.

Deduxit me in Angliam et hortorum celebritas, et inprimis absolutissimum illud Linnæi herbarium vivum, quod in immortalem summi Viri famam, perpetuamque artis botanicæ disciplinam consitum est.

Indefesso quindecim mensium labore, plantas delineandas curavi in suo genere pretiosissimas, non sine magnâ hortorum admiratione, qui et affluenti plantarum copiâ et industriâ colendi, famâ gaudent non immeritâ.

In præsenti fasciculo colliguntur plantæ selectæ et rariores ; uberrimam profecto segetem, quæ peregrinationis curas tanto cum fœnore compensavit! Alias in alia opera remitto, in quibus unaquæque propriis lineamentis, cum plantis congeneribus adumbrabitur.

Genti autem Anglicæ hoc plantarum suarum Sertilegium speciatim offero et dedico. In illos enim laus debet redundare e quibus profecta est. Suadet etiam gratissima animi recordatio quæ semper infra beneficium erit. Juvat enim prædicare, et meminisse amo, quam omnes me comiter exceperint; quam viri doctissimi in explicandâ divitiarum ubertate, se præbuerint faciles et commodos; quam studiosi præsertim homines artis botanicæ officiosam mihi operam navaverint.

Accipiant igitur Angli Botanici, iique soli, nova quæ in hoc opusculo descripsi genera, non ingratum, ut spero, nec ignotum munusculum. Velint meo labori arridere; mihique liceat, ut hoc opus illorum nomine insignitum et vere splendidum, testetur gratum animum æternumque memorem. Dabam Parisiis 20ᵈ Aprilis 1788.

O vale of bliss ! O softly-swelling hills !
On which the *Power of Cultivation* lies ,
And joys to see the wonders of his toil.

. . . .
. . . .
. . . .

. . . .

Happy BRITANNIA ! where the QUEEN OF ARTS ,
Inspiring vigour , LIBERTY abroad
Walks , unconfin'd , even to thy farthest cotes ,
And scatters plenty with unsparing hand.

THOMS. seas.

SYNOPSIS OPERIS.

TETRANDRIA.

WITHERINGIA.

CALYX quadridentatus. *Corolla* campanulata. *Nectarium* quadrilobum, corollæ adnatum, polymorphum. *Stamina* corollæ inserta. *Antheræ* lateribus dehiscentes. *Germen* superum. *Bacca* polysperma.

WITHERINGIA *solanacea.* Tab. 1.

HABITAT *in* . . . . . . ♃

CHLORANTHUS.

PERIANTHIUM duplex. *Exterius :* mera Bractea. *Proprium :* Squamula semisupera, lateri germinis adnata. *Corolla* semisupera, lateralis, dimidiata, trifida, lateri germinis insidens. *Filamenta* nulla. *Antheræ* corollæ adnatæ. *Germen* semiinferum, petaligerum. *Stylus* nullus. *Stigma* capitatum. *Bacca* 1-sperma.

CHLORANTHUS *inconspicuus.* Tab. 2.

Tchu-lan *Chinensibus vulgo.*

HABITAT *in* Chinâ. ♄

PENTANDRIA.

PRISMATOCARPUS.
SPECULARIA. *Heister.* LEGOUSIA. *Durande.*

CALYX, *Corolla, Stamina* ut in Campanulâ. *Germen* inferum, longissimum, polygono-cylindricum. *Stigma* bi-trifidum. *Capsula* prismatico-cylindrica, longissima, bi-trilocularis, polysperma, foraminibus superis emittens *Semina Columellæ* affixa.

Prismatocarpi *genus habitu specierum quamvis placeat, tamen genuinis characteribus* Campanulæ *nimium proximis, forsitan retinendum non erit. Hanc meam sententiam, dum* icon P. nitidi *in lucem prodiet, confirmare novis observatis aut infirmare animus est.*

Eximii quidam Botanici *Prismatocarpum a Campanulâ* genere distinguendum esse jam existimavere. Haller (*hist.* 1. 311.) de *Campanulâ Speculo* agens, his verbis utitur : *vere aliud a Campanulâ genus.* Scopoli (*carn.* 1. 150.) de eâdem plantâ dicit : *flore quasi pentapetalo, rotato, expanso et omnino degenere.*

PENTANDRIA.

1. PRISMATOCARPUS *interruptus.*

P. foliis subulatis ciliatis, ramis floriferis superne interrupte-aphyllis.

HABITAT ad Promontorium bonæ spei. *Thunberg. Oldenburg.*

2. PRISMATOCARPUS *paniculatus.*

P. foliis subulatis subciliatis, paniculis longius pedunculatis.

Polemonium *roëlloides* erectum, caule filiformi, foliis lanceolatis ciliatis, paniculâ pauciflorâ pedunculatâ nudâ. *Linn. suppl.* 139?

HABITAT ad Promontorium bonæ spei. *Andreas Augé.*

Calyces lineares, acutissimi.

Polemonium roëlloides *L. germine infero columnari genus* Prismatocarpi *certe agnoscit, sed omisi dum in Angliâ degebam, cum speciebus novi generis conferre.*

3. PRISMATOCARPUS *altiflorus.*

P. foliis subulatis subciliatis confertissimis, pedunculo longissimo aphyllo, germinibus tomentosis.

HABITAT ad Caput bonæ spei. *Fr. Masson.*

P. interruptus, paniculatus *et* altiflorus *similes foliis et habitu* Lepidii subulati. *Margines foliorum rigidiusculis aculeis muricato-ciliati.*

4. PRISMATOCARPUS *fruticosus.*

P. foliis lineari-subulatis muticis, paniculis terminalibus pedunculatis, caule fruticoso.

Campanula *fruticosa* capsulis quinquelocularibus columnaribus, caule fruticoso, foliis lineari-subulatis, pedunculis longissimis. *Linn. spec.* 238.

HABITAT ad Promontorium bonæ spei. *Masson.* ♄

5. PRISMATOCARPUS *crispus.*

P. foliis linearibus undulatis, caule florifero laxe ramoso, germinibus longissimis.

HABITAT ad Promontorium bonæ spei. *Augé. Masson.*

Calyces *subulati.* Folia *margine revoluta, uti caulis villosa. Facies absolute* Campanulæ undulatæ, *quæ solo germine, ut in aliis* Campanulis, *turbinato brevi distinctissima.*

6. PRISMATOCARPUS *nitidus.* Tab. 3.

P. foliis lanceolatis glaberrimis, floribus terminalibus sessilibus, corollis calyce duplo longioribus.

HABITAT ad Promontorium bonæ spei. *Masson.*

Facies fere Jussievæ.

Differt a congeneribus quæ flore sunt sessili caulibus basi fruticulosis.

7. PRISMATOCARPUS *Speculum.*

P. foliis ovatis , floribus subaxillaribus sessilibus , calycibus corollâ duplo longioribus , caulibus diffusis ramosissimis.

Campanula *Speculum* caule ramosissimo diffuso , foliis oblongis subcrenatis floribus solitariis , capsulis prismaticis. *Linn. ups.* 41.

Onobrychis altera Belgarum et Dodonæi. *Lob. ic.* 418.

Onobrychis prima Dodonæi. *Dalech. hist.* 1. 490.

Viola arvensis. *Tab. ic.* 304.

Pentagonion , viola pentagonia. *Tab. ic.* 316. (optima.)

Campanula arvensis minima. *Dod. pempt.* 168. *Mor. hist.* 2. *sect.* 5. 457. *t.* 2. *f.* 21.

Onobrychis arvensis , vel campanula arvensis erecta. *Bauh. pin.* 215.

Avicularia Sylvii quibusdam. *Bauh. hist.* 2. 800.

Speculum Veneris majus. *Park. theat.* 1331.

Legousia arvensis. *Dur. burg.* 37.

HABITAT in Europæ *mediæ et australis segetibus.* ⊙

Calyces *omnium longiores , nunc lanceolati in junioribus , nunc lineares in senioribus plantis.*

8. PRISMATOCARPUS *hybridus.*

P. foliis oblongis , floribus terminalibus approximatis sessilibus , corollis subclandestinis , caulibus erectis.

Campanula *hybrida* caule basi subramoso stricto , foliis oblongis crenatis , calycibus aggregatis corollâ longioribus, capsulis prismaticis. *Linn. spec.* 239.

Speculum Veneris minus. *Germ. em.* 439. 2. *Park. theat.* 1331.

Campanula arvensis minima erecta. *Mor. hist.* 2. *sect.* 5. 457. *t.* 2. *f.* 22.

HABITAT in Helvetiâ , Angliâ , Galliâ , Carnioliâ *inter segetes.* ⊙

9. PRISMATOCARPUS *Pentagonia.*

P. foliis obovatis , rameis lanceolatis , calycibus pilosis corollâ brevioribus.

Campanula *Pentagonia* caule subdiviso ramosissimo , foliis linearibus acuminatis. *Linn. cliff.* 66.

Campanula pentagonia , flore amplissimo , thracica. *Tourn. inst.* 112.

HABITAT in Thraciâ. ⊙

Planta *pedalis , ramosa , pubescens.* Folia *inferiora* Bellidis, *petiolata , subintegra s. vix obsolete crenulata :* caulina *subsessilia , obverse oblonga , subintegra :* ramea *sessilia , oblonga s. lanceolata , obtusa.* Flores *majusculi.* Germina *corollis longiora.* Calyces *lineares , acuti , pilosiusculi , patentes nec revoluti ut in* P. Speculo.

PENTANDRIA.

LIGHTFOOTIA.

CALYX *semisuperus* , *pentaphyllus.* Corolla *pentapetala.* Valvulæ *staminiferæ ut in* Campanulâ. Germen *inferum simul et superum.* Stigma *tri-quinquefidum.* Capsula *tri-quinquelocularis* , *totvalvis.* Semina *plurima.*

A Campanulâ *differt corollâ pentapetalâ , nec non capsulâ multivalvi.*

1. **LIGHTFOOTIA** *oxycoccoides.* Tab. 4.

L. foliis petalisque lanceolatis.

Lobelia *tenella* caulibus prostratis filiformibus fruticulosis, foliis ovato-lanceolatis glabris utrinque bidentatis. *Linn. mant.* 120. 518.

Campanula *tenella* caulibus diffusis filiformibus , foliis ovatis subunidentatis reflexis , floribus solitariis terminalibus. *Linn. suppl.* 141.

Lobelia parviflora. *Berg. cap.* 354.

HABITAT *ad* Promontorium bonæ spei. *Masson.* ♃

2. **LIGHTFOOTIA** *subulata.* Tab. 5.

L. foliis subulatis , petalis linearibus.

HABITAT *ad* Promontorium bonæ spei. *Masson.*

ROËLLA.

ROËLLA *decurrens.* Tab. 6.

R. herbacea , foliis lanceolatis ciliatis decurrentibus.

HABITAT *ad* Caput bonæ spei. *Masson.* ☉

HAMELIA.

1. **HAMELIA** *patens. L.*

H. foliis subtus tomentosis , tubo corollæ cylindrico.

H. *patens* racemis patentibus. *Jacq. amer.* 72. *t.* 50. *Linn. spec.* 246.

H. *erecta* racemis erectis. *Jacq. amer.* 71 ?

HABITAT *in* Hispaniolâ. ♄

2. **HAMELIA** *grandiflora.* Tab. 7.

H. foliis lævigatis , tubo corollæ ventricoso.

Nerio affinis arbor, versicolorâ materie, lauri folio lucido, flore pentapetaloide sulphureo amplo. *Sloan. hist.* 2. 63. *t.* 183. *f.* 2.

HABITAT *in* Jamaicâ. ♄

RHAMNUS.

CALYX campanulatus, quinquefidus. *Petala* squamiformia, sæpe nulla. *Stamina* petalis cucullata. *Germen* subimmersum. *Stylus* et *Fructus* varii in diversi.

* *Squamulas* linnæanas *Rhamni* petala affirmat analogia. Ita colligendum est ex *Ceanotho,* necnon e *R. Zizipho* et *Paliuro.*

1. **RHAMNUS** *hybridus.*

R. inermis, floribus androgynis, foliis oblongis acuminatis serratis vix perennantibus.

HABITAT in Hortis. ♄

Hanc plantam ultra decennium obtinui e seminibus *R. alpini.* Matrem absolute feminam separatamque a maribus quotannis observavi. *R. Alaternus* certe pater fuit. Semina in nonnullis Galliæ provinciis copiose sata plantam hybridam nec ludentem constanter reddidere.

A Parente utroque tenet. Herba matris. Folia inter R. alpinum *et* Alaternum *media,* substantiâ R. Alaterni *proxima, et fere perennantia. Flores androgyni patris, nec dioici ut in matre.*

2. **RHAMNUS** *alnifolius.*

R. inermis, floribus hermaphroditis, foliis ovalibus acuminatis serratis subtus reticulatis.

HABITAT in Americâ *septentrionali.* ♄

R. alpini *facie sat proximus : sed folia laxius nervosa, magis reticulata, tantummodo glabra nec lucida ut in* R. alpino.

3. **RHAMNUS** *volubilis.* L.

R. inermis, caule volubili, foliis integerrimis ovatis striatis. *Linn. suppl.* 152.

Arbor cheusanensis baccifera, Frangulæ foliis venosa, fructu parvo pyramidali calyculato, ossiculo oblongo binucleo. *Plukn. amalth.* 25. *t.* 368. *f.* 3.

Carpini angustioribus eleganter venosis foliis, planta convolvulacea ex provinciâ Caroliniensi. *Plukn. amalth.* 52. *t.* 435. *f.* 3.

Frutex anonymus foliis dilute virentibus alternis petiolatis lanceolato-oblongis. *Clayt. virg.* 2. 33.

R. scandens. *Hill. kew.* 453. *t.* 20.

HABITAT in Carolinâ. *Garden.* Lodoisiâ. ♄

R. volubilis *et* lineatus *admodum affines. Utrisque flores squamis petaloideis* Rhamni, *drupæ dispermæ nucleis bilocularibus* Corni.

4. **RHAMNUS** *latifolius.* Tab. 8.

R. inermis, floribus monogynis hermaphroditis, calycibus villosis, foliis ellipticis integerrimis.

HABITAT in montibus S^t. Miguel *ex* Azoribus. *Masson.* ♄

R. Frangulæ *simillimus , sed major : calyces villosi ,* in R. Frangulâ *glabri : squamulæ petaloideæ sessiles ,* in R. Frangulâ *subunguiculatæ.*

5. RHAMNUS *prinoides.* Tab. 9.

R. inermis , floribus polygamis , stylo subtriplici , foliis ovatis serratis.

Celtis foliis subrotundis dentatis , flore viridi , fructu luteo. *Burm. afr.* 242. *t.* 18.

HABITAT ad Promontorium bonæ spei. *Augé. Masson.* ♄

6. RHAMNUS *micranthus L.* erit Celtis micrantha in florâ peruanâ.

C E A N O T H U S.

CEANOTHUS *reclinatus.*

C. foliis ovatis integris multinervibus , ramis dependentibus.

Rhamnus arborescens minor , foliis ovatis venosis , pedunculis umbellatis alaribus , fructibus sphæricis. *Brown. jam.* 172. *t.* 29. *f.* 2.

HABITAT in Jamaicâ. *Guillelmus Wright.* ♄

Fructu exsucco absolute Ceanothi , *petalisque fornicatis brevioribus tamen quam in* C. americano , *potius retuli ad* Ceanothum *quam ad* Rhamnum : *sed et totum* Ceanothi *genus rectius ad* Rhamnum *retrahendum erit.*

C E L A S T R U S.

1. CELASTRUS *corniculatus.*

C. foliis ovalibus integerrimis perennantibus , capsulâ tricorni.

Evonymus africanus , foliis laurinis , fructu aculeato. *Breyn. ic. tab.* 22. *f.* 3.

Evonymus foliis subrotundis integris , fructu corniculato. *Burm. afr. t.* 97. *f.* 1.

HABITAT ad Promontorium bonæ spei. ♄

Facies Encleæ.

2. CELASTRUS *cassinoides.* Tab. 10.

C. inermis , foliis ovatis utrinque acutis laxe dentatis perennantibus , floribus axillaribus.

HABITAT in Maderâ , Nivariâ. *Masson.* ♄

3. CELASTRUS *phyllacanthus.*

C. spinis foliosis , foliis lanceolatis serratis perennantibus , floribus lateralibus.

HEXANDRIA.

HABITAT in Senegâ. *Adanson.* ♄

In horto parisiensi floret, sed nondum fructus dedit.

4. **CELASTRUS** *octogonus.*
C. inermis, foliis ellipticis angulatis subenervibus perennantibus, capsulis bivalvibus monospermis.

HABITAT in Peruâ. *Dombey.* ♄

Folia *glauca.* Flores *forte polygami, hermaphroditis aut femineis rarissimis.* Semen *arillatum, bisulcum. Dantur et aliæ species Peruanæ et Cilenses quæ similiter gaudent capsulâ tantum bivalvi.*

5. **CELASTRUS** *undulatus.*
C. inermis, foliis suboppositis lanceolatis undulatis, capsulis bivalvibus polyspermis.

Bois de joli cœur *Gallis vulgo.*

HABITAT in Borboniâ. *Phil. Commerson.* ♄

Folia *lanceolata, acuminata, subuninervia, undulata, margine exalbido revoluto.* Petala *spathulata.* Stigma *obsolete capitatum.* Capsula *unilocularis, bivalvis, polysperma.* Semina 8–12, *nuda nec arillata.*

Planta antisiphylitica. *Commerson.*

Pericarpio et seminibus paululum recedit a *Celastro,* nec satis ut novum constituat genus.

Vigebat olim in horto parisiensi, nunc in horto *Jacobi* LEE, hortulani angli.

HEXANDRIA.

PITCAIRNIA.

CALYX tripartitus, subinferus. *Petala* 3, linearia, convoluta. *Squama* nectarifera ad basim petali. *Filamenta* receptaculo inserta. *Germen* semisuperum, trigonum. *Stylus* trisulcus. *Stigma* trifidum, spirale. *Capsula* semiinfera, trigona, tricocca, introrsum trifariam dehiscens. *Semina* numerosissima, utrinque membranaceo-appendiculata, receptaculo affixa.

PITCAIRNIA *bromeliæfolia.* Tab. 11.

HABITAT in Jamaicâ. ♃

Genus Bromeliæ *et* Tillandsiæ *medium.*

HEXANDRIA.

TRADESCANTIA.

TRADESCANTIA *discolor.* Tab. 12.

T. spathâ triphyllâ compressâ, floribus subexsertis, foliis lanceolatis subtus violaceis.

HABITAT in Americâ *calidâ.* ♃

CRINUM.

COROLLA supera, infundibuliformis, semisexfida. *Tubus* cylindricus. *Limbus* rotatus, æqualis, sexpartitus: *laciniis* linearibus. *Filamenta* fauci inserta, laciniis opposita. *Germen* inferum. *Stylus* filiformis. *Stigma* subtrifidum. *Capsula* trilocularis, trivalvis, polysperma.

Character sistit in tubo cylindrico, limboque æquali. Defectu nectarii tantummodo differt a Pancratio.

1. **CRINUM** *asiaticum. L.*

C. radice bulbosâ, foliis carinatis.

C. foliis carinatis. *Linn. zeyl.* 127. *Mill. ic.* 73. *t.* 110.

Lilium zeylanicum umbelliferum et bulbiferum. *Herm. lugd.b.* 682. *t.* 683.

Belutta-pola-taly. *Rheed. mal.* 11. 75. *t.* 38.

Radix toxicaria. *Rhumph.* 6. 155. *t.* 69. (forte potius synonymon sequentis.)

HABITAT in Malabariâ, Zeylonâ, Tranquebariâ, Americâ *calidâ.* ♃

Stamina *vix declinata.*

2. **CRINUM** *americanum. L.*

C. radice fasciculari.

C. corollarum apicibus introrsum unguiculatis. *Linn. spec.* 419.

Lilio-asphodelus americanus sempervirens maximus polyanthos albus. *Comm. rar.* 14. *t.* 14. *Dill. elth.* 1. 194. *t.* 161.

Lilio-asphodelus americanus sempervirens minor albus. *Comm. rar.* 15. *t.* 15.

HABITAT in Americâ *calidâ.*

3. **CRINUM** *nervosum.*

C. foliis subrotundis nervosis, filamentis basi dilatatis.

Cæpa sylvestris. *Rhumph. amb.* 6. 160. *t.* 70. *f.* 1.

HABITAT in Philippinis. *Poivre.*

Folia *cordato-rotundata, integra, acuminata, nervosa : nervis concentricis.* Scapus

HEXANDRIA.

multiflorus polyphyllus. Flores *longius pedunculati.* Corollæ *infundibuliformes : tubo filiformi ; limbo sexpartito ; laciniis lanceolatis , acutis , patentibus.* Filamenta *fauci inserta, laciniis opposita brevioraque , basi ampliata lata , libera , recta nec declinata mihi visa.*

Crinum latifolium *L.*	*est*	Amaryllis latifolia.
—— zeylanicum *L.*		—— zeylanica.
—— africanum *L.*		Agapanthus umbellatus.
—— tenellum *L.*		Leucoium *ex sententiâ Linnæi* 2[i] *et Solandri , vel forte novum genus.*
—— obliquum *L.*		Amaryllis umbrella.
—— speciosum *L.*		—— speciosa.
—— lineare *L.*		*mihi ignotum.*
—— angustifolium *L.*		Amaryllis cylindracea.
—— falcatum. *Jacq.*		—— falcata.

A M A R Y L L I S.

COROLLA supera , subhexapetaloidea. *Tubus* infundibuliformis , aut subnullus. *Limbus* campanulatus , sexpartitus , irregularis. *Filamenta* basi laciniarum inserta , declinata , inæqualia proportione vel directione. *Germen* inferum. *Stylus* declinatus. *Stigma* trifidum. *Capsula* trilocularis , trivalvis , polysperma.

Essentiam generis administrat directio vel proportio inæqualis filamentorum.

* *Corollis regularibus , filamentis alternis brevioribus.*

1. A M A R Y L L I S *lutea. L.*
A. spathâ uniflorâ indivisâ , corollâ æquali sessili , stigmate simplici.
A. spathâ uniflorâ , corollâ æquali , staminibus declinatis. *Linn. cliff.* 135.
A. spathâ uniflorâ , corollâ æquali , staminibus strictis. *Linn. syst.* 236.
Narcissus autumnalis major. *Clus. hist.* 1. 163. *t.* 164.
Colchicum luteum majus. *Bauh. pin.* 69. *Rudb. elys.* 2. *p.* 129. *f.* 1.
Lilio-narcissus virgineus. *Weinm. phyt.* 3. *p.* 276. *t.* 652. *f.* C.
HABITAT Monspelii , *in* Hispaniâ , Italiâ , Thraciâ. ♃
A genere paululum recedit.

2. A M A R Y L L I S *tubispatha.*
A. spathâ monophyllâ tubulosâ bifidâ uniflorâ , pedunculo spathâ duplo longiore.
HABITAT in Bonariâ. *Commerson.*

H E X A N D R I A.

Scapus *uniflorus , erectus , quadripollicaris.* Spatha *medium fere scapum occupans , tubulosa ,* *cylindracea , bifida , laciniis oppositis.* Flos *longius pedunculatus , erectus.* Filamenta *alterna* 3 *breviora mihi visa.* Folia *in speciminibus Commersonianis non exstabant.*

3. A M A R Y L L I S *tubiflora.*

A. spathâ uniflorâ diphyllâ , corollâ infundibuliformi , tubo longissimo.

Lilio-narcissus croceus monanthos. *Feuill. obs.* 3. 29. *tab.* 20.

Narcissus peruvianus montanus. *Feuill. mss.* 48.

H A B I T A T Limæ , Chancaæ *in arenosis. Dombey.*

Filamenta æqualia dicit Dombejus : subæqualia mihi visa , sed specimen haud *optimum observavi.*

4. A M A R Y L L I S *spiralis.* Tab. 13.

A. spathâ diphyllâ pauciflorâ , pedunculis filiformibus longissimis , foliis subulatis.

H A B I T A T in arenosis Capitis bonæ spei. *Bruguiere.*

Corolla *sexpartita , limbo patentissimo æquali , tubo brevi.* Filamenta *erecta ,* *alterna breviora.* Scapus *basi tortilis.*

** *Limbo corollæ campanulato irregulari , genitalibus declinatis.*

5. A M A R Y L L I S *Atamasco. L.*

A. spathâ uniflorâ bifidâ , corollâ subæquali , genitalibus declinatis.

A. spathâ uniflorâ , corollâ æquali , pistillo refracto. *Linn. cliff.* 135.

Lilio-narcissus indicus pumilus monanthos albus. *Mor. hist.* 2. *p.* 366. *sect.* 4. *t.* 24. *f.* 4.

Lilio-narcissus s. narcissus liliflorus carolinianus , flore albo singulari cum rubedine diluto. *Plukn. almag.* 220. *t.* 142. *f.* 3.

Lilio-narcissus vernus angustifolius , flore purpurascente. *Barrel. ic.* 994.

Lilio-narcissus minimus , foliis gramineis. *Rudb. elys.* 2. 94. *t.* 16.

Lilio-narcissus indicus albus. *Weinm. phyt.* 3. *p.* 276. *t.* 652. *f.* 6.

Lilio-narcissus virginiensis. *Catesb. car.* 3. *p.* 12. *t.* 12.

Lilio-narcissus VI. *Trew. seligm.. tab.* 37.

H A B I T A T in Americâ *septentrionali.* 4

6. A M A R Y L L I S *maculata.*

A. spathâ uniflorâ diphyllâ lineari , flore pedunculato , genitalibus declinatis.

H A B I T A T in Chile. *Dombey.*

Scapus *punctis lineatis maculatus.* Corolla *campanulata.*

HEXANDRIA.

7. AMARYLLIS *chilensis.*

A. spathâ uni-biflorâ subbifoliâ lanceolatâ , floribus pedunculatis , foliis linearibus.

Lilio-narcissus monanthos coccineus. *Feuill. obs.* 3. *t.* 21. (absque foliis.) *mss.* *p.* 5o. (cum foliis.)

HABITAT in Chile. *Dombey.*

Flores *A. Belladonnæ aut reginæ , purpurei.*

8. AMARYLLIS *clavata.*

A. spathâ uniflorâ diphyllâ subulatâ , corollâ clavatâ.

HABITAT in Africâ *australi.*

Flos *pedicellatus.* Tubus *basi angustus , non dilatatus.* Limbus *brevissimus.*

Folia non vidi , nec stamina observarè licuit : an hujus vel præcedentis sectionis incertum remanet.

9. AMARYLLIS *formosissima.* L.

A. spathâ indivisâ uniflorâ , corollâ bilabiatâ sexpartitâ , petalis inferioribus genitalibusque dependentibus.

A. spathâ uniflorâ , corollâ inæquali , genitalibus declinatis. *Linn. cliff.* 135. *act. holm.* 1742. 93. *t.* 6.

A. spathâ uniflorâ , corollâ inæquali , petalis tribus genitalibusque declinatis. *Linn. spec.* 420.

Narcissus latifolius indicus rubro flore. *Clus. hist.* 1. 157. *cur.* 12. *Bauh. hist.* 2. 609.

Narcissus indicus flore sanguineo. *Swertz. flor. t.* 28.

Narcissus indicus totus ruber. *Bauh. pin.* 49.

Lilio-narcissus jacobæus latifolius indicus , rubro flore. *Mor. hist.* 2. *p.* 366. *sect.* 4. *t.* 10. *f.* 31.

Lilio-narcissus indicus ruber monanthos jacobæus. *Barrel. icon. t.* 1035.

Lilio-narcissus jacobæus , flore sanguineo nutante. *Dill. elth.* 195. *t.* 162.

Lilio-narcissus indicus totus ruber vulgo jacobæus. *Weinm. phyt.* 3. *p.* 276. *t.* 652. *f.* A.

Narcissus jacobæus. *Trew. seligm. t.* 24.

HABITAT in Mexico. 4

Corollam polypetalam mentitur , sed Petala *reverâ basi unita , staminaque iis inserta ut in congeneribus : tria inferiora dependentia.* Faux *obsolete ramentacea.*

10. AMARYLLIS *reginæ.*

A. spathâ subbiflorâ , corollis basi tubulosis campanulatis quinquepartitis , fauce tubi hirsutâ.

Lilium americanum puniceo flore, Belladonna dictum. *Herm. par. p.* 194 *t.* 194.

Lilio-narcissus indicus, seu narcissus liliflorus aureus striis argenteis pictus, floribus amplis cernuis gemellis, caule magno cæpæ fistuloso. *Plukn. almag.* 220. *t.* 246. *f.* 2.

Lilio-narcissus polyanthos, flore incarnato, fundo ex luteo albescente. *Sloan. cat.* 115. *Mer. sur.* 22. *t.* 22. *Seb. thes.* 25. *t.* 17. *f.* 1.

A. spathâ multiflorâ, corollis campanulatis marginibus reflexis, genitalibus declinatis. *Mill. ic.* 16. *t.* 23.

Lilio-narcissus 11. *Trew. seligm. t.* 18.

A. dubia. *Linn. amœn.* 8. 254.

HABITAT in Jamaicâ, Surinamo. ♃

11. AMARYLLIS *speciosa.*

A. spathâ subbiflorâ, corollis erectis basi tubulosis campanulatis semiquinquefidis, fauce tubi glabrâ.

Crinum *speciosum* foliis uniformibus, corollis campanulatis, tribus laciniis alternis calloso-unguiculatis. *Linn. suppl.* 195.

HABITAT in Africâ *australi. Masson.*

Quam plurimum affinis præcedenti. An satis distincta ?

12. AMARYLLIS *reticulata.* Tab. 14.

A. spathâ submultiflorâ, corollis nutantibus basi tubulosis limbo reticulatis, foliis oblongis.

HABITAT in Brasiliâ ?

Petalis transverse venosis distincta. Faux glabra.

13. AMARYLLIS *Belladonna.*

A. floribus umbellatis pedunculatis subhexapetalis, foliis canaliculatis.

Lilio-narcissus rubens indicus. *Ald. farn.* 83. *t.* 82.

Lilio-narcissus pumilus indicus polyanthos. *Corn. can.* 153. *t.* 154.

Narcissus indicus liliaceus diluto colore purpurascens. *Ferr. flor.* 117. *tab.* 121. 123.

Narcissus indicus liliaceus saturo colore purpurascens. *Ferr. flor. t.* 119.

Narcissus indicus polyanthos liliaceo flore. *Rudb. elys.* 2. *p.* 48. *f.* 7. (figura Ferrarii.)

Lilio-asphodelus capensis, flore roseo. *Pet. gaz. n.* 497. *t.* 85. *f.* 5.

Lilio-narcissus jacobæus phœniceus indicus polyanthos. *Barrel. rar.* 69. *t.* 1036.

Lilio-narcissus indicus saturate purpurascens polyanthos Belladonaformos italicus. *Barrel. rar.* 70. *t.* 1039.

Lilio-narcissus indicus dilute purpurascens, Belladona italorum vulgatior. *Barrel. rar.* 70. *t.* 1040.

Lilio-narcissus indicus, flore elegantissime purpurascente. *Weinm. phyt.* 3. *pag.* 276. *t.* 653. *f. A.*

A. spathâ multiflorâ, corollis campanulatis æqualibus, genitalibus declinatis. *Mill. ic.* 15. *t.* 23.

A. Belladonna. *Mill. illust.*

HABITAT ad Promontorium bonæ spei. ♃

Laciniæ *alternæ extrorsum manifestissime uncinatæ.* Stigma *trifidum.*

14. AMARYLLIS *vittata.* Tab. 15.

A. spathâ multiflorâ, floribus pedunculatis subhexapetalis, petalis exterioribus margine liberis.

HABITAT in . . . . ♃

Petala *inferne connata in tubum carnosum, sed margines exteriorum ad basin liberi.*

15. AMARYLLIS *falcata.*

A. floribus umbellatis longius pedunculatis sexpartitis, foliis falcatis margine cartilagineo muricato discolore.

Crinum falcatum. *Jacq. hort.* 3. 34. *t.* 60.

HABITAT ad Promontorium bonæ spei.

16. AMARYLLIS *longifolia. L.*

A. floribus umbellatis pedunculatis basi tubulosis sexpartitis, foliis scapo duplo longioribus.

A. spathâ multiflorâ, corollis campanulatis æqualibus, genitalibus declinatis, scapo compresso longitudine umbellæ. *Linn. spec.* 421.

Lilio-narcissus africanus platicaulis humilis, flore purpurascente odorato. *Comm. hort.* 1. 71. *t.* 36.

Lilium africanum humile, longissimis foliis, polyanthos saturato colore purpurascens. *Herm. par. pag.* et *tab.* 195.

Lilio-narcissus africanus laticaulis humilis. *Rudb. elys.* 2. *p.* 180. *f.* 8. (icon Commelini.)

HABITAT ad Promontorium bonæ spei.

17. AMARYLLIS *zeylanica. L.*

A. spathâ multiflorâ, corollis reclinatis, tubo filiformi longissimo, laciniis uncinatis.

A. *zeylanica* spathâ multiflorâ, corollis campanulatis æqualibus, genitalibus declinatis , scapo tereti ancipiti. *Linn. spec.* 421.

Crinum *zeylanicum* foliis scabro-dentatis , scapo compressiusculo. *Linn. syst.* 236.

Lilio-narcissus ceylanicus latifolius, flore niveo externe lineâ purpureâ striato. *Comm. hort.* 1. 73. *t.* 37.

Lilio-narcissus zeylanicus latifolius. *Rudb. elys.* 2. 181. *f.* 9. (icon Commelini.)

Tulipa javana. *Rhumph. amb.* 5. 306. *t.* 105.

Lilio-narcissus africanus , scillæ foliis , flore niveo lineâ purpureâ striato. *Ehret. pict.* 5. *f.* 2 ? *Trew. ehret.* 3. *tab.* 13 ?

A. *bulbisperma* spathâ multiflorâ , corollis campanulatis æqualibus , genitalibus declinatis , pericarpio bulbigero. *Burm. prodr.* 19.

H A B I T A T in Indiâ *orientali.* ♃

Pericarpia vivipara.

18. A M A R Y L L I S *revoluta.*

A. spathâ multiflorâ , corollis breviter pedicellatis basi tubulosis reclinatis , laciniis corollæ revolutis , foliis linearibus.

H A B I T A T ad Promontorium bonæ spei.

19. A M A R Y L L I S *latifolia.*

A. spathâ multiflorâ , floribus pedicellatis subreclinatis basi tubulosis , foliis oblongo–lanceolatis.

Crinum *latifolium* foliis ovato-lanceolatis acuminatis sessilibus planis. *Linn. sp.* 419.

Sjovanna-pola-tali. *Rheed. mal.* 11. 77. *t.* 39.

H A B I T A T in Indiâ *orientali.*

Plantam non vidi.

20. A M A R Y L L I S *aurea.* Tab. 15 *bis.*

A. spathâ multiflorâ , corollis basi tubulosis sexpartitis , laciniis linearibus undulatis , genitalibus corollâ longioribus.

H A B I T A T in Chinâ. ♃

Folia *lato-linearia* , *læte viridia.* Scapus *pedalis* , *quinque-sexflorus.* Flores *breviter pedicellati* , *fulvi.* Petala *angusta* , *inferne distantia* , *undulata.* Stigma *simplex.*

21. A M A R Y L L I S *orientalis. L.*

A. umbellâ multiflorâ , floribus longissime pedunculatis sexpartitis , germinibus cuneiformibus triangularibus , foliis ovatis.

A. spathâ multiflorâ , corollis inæqualibus , foliis linguiformibus. *Linn. spec.* 422.

Narcissus indicus orientalis. *Swert. flor.* 31. *f.* 1.

Narcissus indicus , flore liliaceo , sphæricus. *Ferr. flor.* 125. *t.* 129. 131. 133.

HEXANDRIA.

Lilio-narcissus indicus maximus sphæricus, floribus plurimis rubris liliaceis. *Mor. hist.* 2. *p.* 368. *sect.* 4. *t.* 10. *f.* 35. (figura Ferrarii.)

Brunsvigia. *Heist. monogr. cum iconibus.*

HABITAT *in* Indiâ *orientali.* ♃

22. AMARYLLIS *ciliaris.* L.

A. spathâ multiflorâ, corollâ sexpartitâ reflexâ, foliis ciliatis. *Linn. suppl.* 195.

A. *ciliaris* spathâ multiflorâ, foliis ciliatis. *Linn. spec.* 422.

A. *guttata* spathâ multiflorâ, foliis ciliatis. *Linn. syst.* 237.

Hæmanthus *ciliaris* foliis linguiformibus ciliatis. *Linn. spec.* 413.

Bulbus oblongus æthiopicus, foliis guttatis et cilii instar pilosis. *Breyn. cent.* 89. *t.* 39.

Lilium africanum sphæricum, floribus obsolete puniceis minoribus, foliis guttatis ad margines cilii instar pilosis, bulbo oblongo. *Herm. lugdb.* 375.

Lilio-narcissus sphæricus æthiopicus, foliis guttatis et cilii instar pilosis. *Plukn. almag.* 220.

HABITAT *ad* Promontorium bonæ spei. ♃

An sit Amaryllis, *vel potius* Hæmanthus, *an duæ sint reverá plantæ adhuc incertum est. Unicam scilicet breynianam vivam nec florentem novi.*

23. AMARYLLIS *Umbella.* Tab. 16.

A. umbellâ reclinatâ, corollis incurvis infundibulo-tubulosis, limbo sexfido erecto, genitalibus inclusis.

Crinum *obliquum* foliis lanceolatis obliquis, laciniis corollæ alternis extus glandulosis. *Linn. suppl.* 195.

HABITAT *ad* Promontorium bonæ spei. *Masson.* ♃

Flores *cernui.* Tubus *corollæ turbinatus.* Limbus *campanulatus, erectus.*

24. AMARYLLIS *cylindracea.*

A. spathâ multiflorâ, corollis infundibuliformibus, tubo elongato cylindrico subincurvo, foliis linearibus.

Crinum *angustifolium* foliis linearibus obtusis, corollis cylindricis, laciniis alternis interglandulosis. *Linn. suppl.* 195.

HABITAT *ad* Promontorium bonæ spei. *Masson, Oldenburg.*

* * * *Corollis radiatis, tubo subnullo.*

25. AMARYLLIS *sarniensis.* L.

A. spathâ multiflorâ, corollis subhexapetalis lineari-lanceolatis, genitalibus rectiusculis exsertis.

HEXANDRIA.

A. spathâ multiflorâ, corollis revolutis, genitalibus strictis. *Linn. ups.* 75. *Thunb. jap.* 131.

A. spathâ multiflorâ, corollis æqualibus patentissimis revolutis, genitalibus longissimis. *Linn. cliff.* 135.

Narcissus japonicus rutilo flore. *Corn. can.* 157. *t.* 158. *Ehret. pict. t.* 9.

Lilio–narcissus japonicus rutilo flore. *Mor. hist.* 2. *p.* 367. *Seb. thes.* 1. 25. *t.* 17. *f.* 3.

Seki san. *Kœmpf. amœn.* 872.

Lilio–narcissus 4. *Trew. seligm. t.* 30.

HABITAT in Japoniâ. *ad* Caput bonæ spei. *Masson, Oldenburg.* ♃

26. AMARYLLIS *radiata.*

A. spathâ multiflorâ, corollis subhexapetalis linearibus undulatis **revolutis**, genitalibus deflexis divergentibus, corollâ duplo longioribus.

Lilio–narcissus v. *Trew. seligm. t.* 35. (nisi exhibeat quamdam *A. sarniensis* varietatem.)

HABITAT in . . . . ♃

27. AMARYLLIS *cinnamomea.* Tab. 17.

A. spathâ multiflorâ, corollis subhexapetalis lanceolatis undulatis, genitalibus erectis corollâ brevioribus.

Caneel bloem *Belgis vulgo.*

HABITAT ad Promontorium bonæ spei. *Bruguiere.* ♃

Flores *dimidio minores quam in A. undulatâ.* Petala *duplo latiora quorum exteriora magis revoluta.* Stigma *simplex.* Hæmanthi *affinis.*

28. AMARYLLIS *undulata. L.*

A. spathâ multiflorâ, corollis subhexapetalis linearibus canaliculatis undulatis, genitalibus deflexis corollâ brevioribus.

A. spathâ multiflorâ, corollis patulis, petalis undulatis mucronatis basi dilatatis. *Linn. syst.* 237.

A. undulata. *Hill. kew.* 352. *tab.* 14. *Jacq. hort.* 3. 11. *tab.* 13. *Meerb. icon.* 13. *J. F. Mill. ic.* 8.

HABITAT ad Promontorium bonæ spei. ♃

Stigma *capitatum.* Pericarpium *viviparum.*

A. spiralis tubo brevissimo limboque rotato æquali hîc collocari poterat, sed staminibus alternis brevioribus ad primam sectionem revocavi.

Amaryllis capensis *L. est* Hypoxis stellata. *Linn. suppl.* 197,

———— disticha. *L.* Hæmanthus ?

H E X A N D R I A.

A G A P A N T H U S.

S P A T H A polyphylla. *Corolla* infera , infundibuliformis , regularis , sexpartita. *Tubus* brevis. *Laciniæ* oblongæ s. spathulatæ , patentes. *Filamenta* tubo superne inserta , laciniis opposita , declinata. *Antheræ* biloculares , peltatæ. *Germen* superum , trigonum. *Stylus* staminibus conformis. *Stigma* subcapitatum. *Capsula* triangularis , trilocularis , trivalvis. *Semina* plurima, apice imbricata alata.

A G A P A N T H U S *umbellatus.*

Crinum *africanum* foliis sublanceolatis planis , corollis obtusis. *Linn. spec.* 419.

Hyacinthus africanus tuberosus , flore cæruleo umbellato. *Breyn. prodr.* 1. 25. *icon.* 23. *t.* 10. *f.* 1. *Trew. comm. litter. anno* 1744. *p.* 351. *t.* 4. *f.* 3. 9. 10. *Comm. hort.* 2. 133. *t.* 67. *Seb. thes.* 1. 29. *t.* 19. *f.* 4.

Hyacintho affinis , tuberosâ radice , africana , umbellâ cæruleâ inodorâ. *Plukn. almag.* 187. *t.* 295. *f.* 1.

Polyanthes floribus umbellatis. *Linn. vir.* 29. *cliff.* 126. *Mill. ic.* 140. *t.* 210. *Ehret. pict. t.* 10.

H A B I T A T ad Promontorium bonæ spei. 4

Flores absolute Hemerorallidis , *sed spathâ genus distinctum.*

E U C O M I S.

C A L Y X nullus. *Corolla* sexpartita. *Filamenta* subulata , basi dilatata , ibique coalita in *Nectarium* concavum fundo corollæ adnatum. *Germen* superum. *Stigma* simplex. *Capsula* trilocularis , polysperma.

1. E U C O M I S *regia.*
E. scapo cylindrico , comâ maximâ foliosiore , foliis undulatis.
Fritillaria *regia* racemo comoso inferne nudo , foliis crenatis. *Linn. spec.* 435.
Corona regalis lilii folio crenato. *Dill. elth.* 1. 109. *t.* 93.
Fritillaria longifolia. *Hill. kew.* 354. *t.* 15.
H A B I T A T ad Promontorium bonæ spei. 4

2. E U C O M I S *nana.*
E. scapo clavato , floribus confertissimis.
Fritillaria *nana* racemo comoso , foliis bifariis amplexicaulibus lanceolatis. *Burm. prodr.* 9.
Orchidea capensis , tulipæ flore rosaceo. *Pet. gaz. t.* 85. *f.* 6.

HABITAT ad Promontorium bonæ spei. *Masson.* ♃

Frondescentia Massoniæ. *Folia ovata, acuminata, subtus lineata: venis apice confluentibus.*

3. **EUCOMIS** *punctata.* Tab. 18.

E. maculata, scapo cylindrico elongato laxifloro, foliis ensiformibus canaliculatis.

Asphodelus comosus. *Houtt. nat. hist.* 12. *pag.* 336. *tab.* 83.

HABITAT ad Promontorium bonæ spei. ♃

Coma minor minusque foliosa quam in cæteris, pedunculi longiores laxiores.

E. nana *minor est,* E. regia *media,* E. punctata *major.*

OCTANDRIA.

KOËLREUTERIA.

PERIANTHIUM pentaphyllum. *Petala* 4, quorum infera 2 opposita. *Nectarium* duplex: *Squamulæ* 4, bipartitæ, unguibus petalorum adnatæ, coronam faucis constituentes: *Glandulæ* 3, inter stamina et pistillum. *Filamenta* subdeclinata, columnæ genitali affixa. *Germen* triquetrum, columnâ genitali elevatum. *Stylus* trigonus. *Stigma* trifidum. *Capsula* trilocularis: *loculis* dispermis.

KOËLREUTERIA *paullinioides.* Tab. 19.

K. paniculata. *Laxm. nov. comm. petr.* 16. *p.* 561. *t.* 18.

Sapindus *chinensis* foliis pinnatis, foliolis laciniatis. *Murr. syst.* 315. *Linn. suppl.* 228.

HABITAT in Chinâ. ♄

Arbor polygama.

ICOSANDRIA.

EUCALYPTUS.

PERIANTHIUM: Operculum superum, integerrimum, truncatum. *Petalum: Calyptra* obverse hemisphærica, margini calycis imposita, ante anthesin discedens. *Filamenta* numerosissima, calyci inserta. *Germen* inferum, turbinatum. *Stylus* unicus. *Capsula* subquadrilocularis, apice duntaxat dehiscens. *Semina* plurima, angulata.

EUCALYPTUS *obliqua.* Tab. 20.

HABITAT in Novâ Cambriâ. *Nelson. Guil. Anderson.* ♄

DIDYNAMIA.

LAVANDULA.

LAVANDULA *viridis.* Tab. 21.

L. foliis sessilibus linearibus rugosis villosis margine revolutis, spicâ comosâ, bracteis indivisis.

HABITAT in Maderâ. *Masson.* ♃

Differt a L. stæchade *foliis rugosis villosis viridibus nec tomentosis canis, bracteis comâque integris viridibus nec subtrilobis purpurascentibus.*

BYSTROPOGON.

CALYX monophyllus, quinquesubulatus, fauce barbatus. *Corolla* ringens. *Labium superius* bifidum : *inferius* trifidum ; laciniâ extimâ productiore. *Filamenta* didynama, distantia. *Germen* superum, quadripartitum. *Stigma* bifidum. *Calyx* barbâ clausus, in fundo *Semina* quatuor fovens.

1. **BYSTROPOGON** *pectinatum.*
   B. paniculis compactis, floribus secundis, foliis ovatis.
   Nepeta *pectinata* spicis secundis, foliis cordatis nudis, caule frutescente, corollis minutis. *Linn. spec.* 799.
   Nepeta maxima, flore albo, spicâ habitiori. *Sloan. jam.* 65. *hist.* 1. 173. *t.* 108. *f.* 1. (mala, nisi erronea. In herbario *Sloanei* adglutinatur *B. pectinatum,* sed icon sistit plantam alienam ad genus *Hypteos* Jacquini forte referendam.)
   Galeopsis procerior foliis ovato-acuminatis serratis, spicis majoribus compositis terminalibus, spicillis geminatis uno versu floridis. *Brown. jam.* 259.
   HABITAT in Peruâ. *Dombey.* Jamaicâ.

2. **BYSTROPOGON** *sidæfolium.*
   B. paniculis laxissimis, pedunculis verticillatis filiformibus, foliis cordatis.
   HABITAT in Peruâ. *Dombey.*

3. **BYSTROPOGON** *suaveolens.*
   B. pedunculis axillaribus solitariis, calycibus truncatis aristatis, foliis cordatis.
   Ballota *suaveolens* foliis cordatis, spicis foliosis, calycibus truncatis aristis linearibus. *Linn. spec.* 815.
   Melissa jamaicana odoratissima. *Plukn. almag.* 247. *t.* 306. *f.* 3.
   Melissa spicata lavandulam spirans major. *Plum. cat.* 6. *ic.* 155. *t.* 163. *f.* 1.

D I D Y N A M I A.

Mentastrum maximum flore cæruleo, nardi odore. *Sloan. jam.* 64. *hist.* 1. 171. *t.* 102. *f.* 2.

Mesosphærum hirsutum foliis cordatis serrato-sinuatis , floribus verticaliter spicatis. *Brown. jam.* 257. *t.* 18. *f.* 3.

H A B I T A T in Americâ *meridionali.*

4. B Y S T R O P O G O N *plumosum.* Tab. 22.

B. paniculis dichotomis , calycibus plumosis , foliis ovatis subserratis subtus tomentosis.

Mentha *plumosa* caule fruticoso , foliis ovatis petiolatis serratis subtus albotomentosis , paniculis dichotomis terminalibus. *Linn. suppl.* 273.

H A B I T A T in Canariis , Nivariâ. *Masson.* ♄

B. plumosum *et* origanifolium *jungunt* B. canariense *et* punctatum *præcedentibus.*

5. B Y S T R O P O G O N *origanifolium.*

B. paniculis dichotomis , calycibus plumosis , foliis ovatis integerrimis subtus candidissimis.

H A B I T A T in Nivariâ. *Masson.* ♄

Admodum affinis præcedenti , sed folia integerrima subtus nivea.

6. B Y S T R O P O G O N *canariense.*

B. pedunculis dichotomis , floribus capitatis , foliis ovatis crenatis subtus villosioribus.

Mentha floribus capitatis ex alis , foliis ovatis crenatis , caule arborescente. *Linn. cliff.* 307.

Mentha *canariensis* floribus capitatis axillaribus dichotomis , staminibus corollâ brevioribus , foliis ovatis crenatis , caule arborescente. *Linn. spec.* 807.

Mentha canariensis frutescens , foliis subtus lanugine candidissimâ villosis , floribus glomeratis e sinu foliorum longioribus pediculis insidentibus. *Plukn. almag.* 248. *t.* 307. *f.* 2.

Heliotropium canariense arborescens , scorodoniæ folio. *Comm. hort.* 2. 129. *t.* 65.

Heliotropium *canariense* foliis ovatis crenatis oppositis, floribus capitatis alaribus dichotomis , caule arborescente. *Mill. dict. n.* 5.

H A B I T A T in Maderâ , Nivariâ. *Masson.* ♄

7. B Y S T R O P O G O N *punctatum.* Tab. 23.

B. pedunculis dichotomis , floribus capitatis , foliis ovatis dentatis glabris punctulatis.

H A B I T A T in Maderâ. *Banks et Solander , Masson.* ♄

Laciniæ calycinæ non. subulatæ ut in cœteris ; nihilominus congener.

DIADELPHIA. SYNGENESIA.

DIGITALIS.

DIGITALIS *Sceptrum. L.* Tab. 24.

D. foliis oblongis spathulatis serratis , spicis oblongis pedunculatis apice comosis , caule fruticoso.

D. *Sceptrum* fruticosa , foliis oblongis spathulatis serratis , spicis terminalibus ovatis pedunculatis comâ bractearum terminatis , calycinis foliolis subulatis , corollis quadrifidis. *Linn. suppl.* 282.

HABITAT *in sylvis umbrosis* Maderæ. *Masson.* ♄

CAPRARIA.

CAPRARIA *undulata. L.* Tab. 25.

C. foliis sparsis inæqualiter approximatis ovatis integris subundulatis , racemo terminali subsimplici.

C. *undulata* foliis alternis ovatis undulatis , racemis secundis. *Linn. suppl.* 284.

HABITAT *in collibus prope* Swellendam *ad* Caput bonæ spei. *Masson.* ♄

Folia nonnulla quasi verticillata.

DIADELPHIA.

ASPALATHUS.

ASPALATHUS *pedunculata.* Tab. 26.

A. foliis fasciculatis subulatis glabris , pedunculis filiformibus folio duplo longioribus.

HABITAT *ad* Promontorium bonæ spei. *Masson.* ♄

SYNGENESIA.

TANACETUM.

TANACETUM *flabelliforme.* Tab. 27.

T. corymbis simplicibus , foliis deltoidibus apice serratis.

HABITAT *ad* Promontorium bonæ spei. *Masson.* ♃

Flosculi *omnes hermaphroditi quinquefidi , sed receptaculo nudo nec paleaceo potius quadrat cum* Tanaceto , *quam cum* Athanasiâ.

SYNGENESIA.

ARTEMISIA.

ARTEMISIA *argentea.* Tab. 28.

A. fruticosa sericea , foliis subpalmatis pinnatisve , laciniis lato-linearibus remotis.

HABITAT in Maderâ. *Masson.* ♄

Tota argentea. Receptaculum *villosum.*

RELHANIA.

CALYX communis oblongus, imbricatus , squamatus , scariosus. *Corolla* radiata. *Corollulæ hermaphroditæ* numerosæ, in disco : *femineæ* plurimæ , in radio. *Filamenta* hermaphroditis quinque. *Anthera* tubulosa. *Germen* utrisque oblongiusculum. *Stylus* unicus. *Stigmata* 2 , revoluta. *Calyx* immutatus in *Pericarpium. Semina* solitaria. *Pappus* membranaceus , multifidus vel lacerus. *Receptaculum* paleaceum.

Differt ab Athanasiâ *tantum corollâ radiatâ , nec æquali. Potuissent itaque* Relhaniæ *uti sectio distincta* Athanasiis *sociari, suadente* Senecione *aliisque generibus. Distinguitur a* Leyserâ *pappo membranaceo , nec plumoso : ab* Osmite *flosculis femineis fertilibus , calyce scarioso.*

* *Floribus aggregatis.*

1. RELHANIA *squarrosa.* Tab. 29.
   R. foliis oblongis acuminatis enervibus apice recurvis.
   Athanasia *squarrosa* pedunculis unifloris lateralibus , foliis ovalibus recurvatis. *Linn. amœn.* 4. 329. *et* 6. 52.
   HABITAT ad Promontorium bonæ spei. *Masson.* ♄

2. RELHANIA *genistifolia.*
   R. foliis lanceolatis acuminatis uninervibus subimbricatis.
   Athanasia *genistifolia* corymbis simplicibus , foliis lanceolatis indivisis nudis confertis. *Linn. mant.* 464.
   HABITAT ad Promontorium bonæ spei. *Masson , Kœnig.* ♄

3. RELHANIA *microphylla.*
   R. foliis linearibus enervibus confertissimis , floribus pedicellatis.
   HABITAT ad Promontorium bonæ spei. *Masson.* ♄

4. **RELHANIA** *passerinoides.*

R. foliis linearibus enervibus, floribus subsessilibus.

H A B I T A T ad Caput bonæ spei. *Masson.* ♄

Folia floresque duplo majora quam in R. microphyllâ : *caules erecti , nec diffusi.*

5. **RELHANIA** *viscosa.*

R. foliis linearibus triquetris carnosiusculis viscidis.

H A B I T A T ad Promontorium bonæ spei. *Masson.* ♄

R. viscosa *et* passerinoides *inflorescentiâ habituque admodum affines sed in* R. viscosâ *folia quasi trigona , subcarnosa , adspersa glandulis pedicellatis quibus* R. passerinoides *destituitur.*

* * *Floribus solitariis.*

6. **RELHANIA** *laxa.*

R. foliis linearibus villosis remotis , floribus longius pedunculatis , caule erecto.

H A B I T A T ad Promontorium bonæ spei. *Masson.* ☉

7. **RELHANIA** *pedunculata.*

R. foliis linearibus villosis , floribus pedunculatis , caulibus diffusis.

Zoegea *capensis* foliis linearibus , calyce glabro basi gibbo. *Linn. suppl.* 382.

Athanasia *pumila* foliis linearibus pilosis, pedunculis unifloris folio longioribus. *Linn. suppl.* 362.

H A B I T A T ad Promontorium bonæ spei.

8. **RELHANIA** *lateriflora.*

R. foliis linearibus villosis , pedunculis lateralibus folio brevioribus.

Athanasia *sessiliflora* foliis linearibus pilosis, pedunculis unifloris folio brevioribus. *Linn. suppl.* 362.

H A B I T A T ad Promontorium bonæ spei. *Masson.*

9. **RELHANIA** *cuneata.*

R. foliis obovatis glabris , floribus sessilibus.

Athanasia *uniflora* foliis obovatis imbricatis glabris , floribus terminalibus sessilibus solitariis. *Linn. suppl.* 362.

H A B I T A T ad Promontorium bonæ spei. *Masson.* ♄

10. **RELHANIA** *virgata.*

R. foliis linearibus glabris , **acumine recurvo folio breviore**, floribus sessilibus.

H A B I T A T ad Promontorium bonæ spei. *Masson.* ♄

Admodum affinis præcedenti , cujus forte varietas.

11. R E L H A N I A *paleacea.*

R. foliis linearibus triquetris subtus turionibusque canescentibus , calycibus sessilibus turbinatis.

Leysera *paleacea* foliis triquetris apice callosis recurvatis. *Linn. syst.* 561.

H A B I T A T ad Promontorium bonæ spei. *Masson.* ♄

12. R E L H A N I A *santolinoides.*

R. foliis linearibus triquetris subtus turionibusque incanis , calycibus globosis subpetiolatis.

H A B I T A T ad Promontorium bonæ spei. *Masson.* ♄

An satis distincta a R. paleaceâ ? *In utrâque pappus tubulosus apice dentatus.*

13. R E L H A N I A *pungens.*

R. foliis linearibus subpungentibus subtus striatis , floribus sessilibus.

H A B I T A T ad Promontorium bonæ spei. *Masson.* ♄

14. R E L H A N I A *decussata.*

R. foliis triquetris linearibus acutis decussatis , floribus sessilibus.

H A B I T A T ad Promontorium bonæ spei. *Masson.* ♄

15. R E L H A N I A *calycina.*

R. foliis lineari–lanceolatis subtrinervibus acutis , floribus sessilibus.

Osmites *calycina* foliis lanceolatis nudis , calycibus scariosis. *Linn. suppl.* 380.

H A B I T A T ad Promontorium bonæ spei. *Masson.* ♄

R. pungens , decussata , calycina *gaudent calyce ampliori squamis intimis majoribus.*
Vix idem in R. paleaceâ.

16. R E L H A N I A *Bellidiastrum.*

R. foliis linearibus tomentosis , floribus sessilibus.

Osmites *Bellidiastrum* foliis linearibus tomentosis , calycibus scariosis. *Linn. spec.* 1285.

Bellidiastrum subhirsutum linifolium. *Vaill. act. par.* 1724. *p.* 316.

Anthemis suffruticosa , foliis linearibus triquetris tomentosis indivisis , floribus sessilibus. *Linn. amœn.* 4. 330.

H A B I T A T ad Caput bonæ spei. *Masson.* ♄

Pappus *nullus. A genere sat aliena.*

SYNGENESIA.

CINERARIA.

1. **CINERARIA** *humifusa.*

C. pedunculis unifloris, foliis reniformibus subangulatis, petiolis apice auriculatis nudisve.

Aster flore luteo, foliis cymbalariæ. *Rai. hist.* 3. 158.

Aster africanus minimus monanthos luteus, foliolis angulosis minimis aceris formâ vel cymbalariæ. *Rai. hist.* 3. 161.

HABITAT ad Promontorium bonæ spei. *Masson.* ♄

Affinis C. cymbalarifoliæ, *sed flores lutei calycesque villoso-scabriusculi, dum flores purpurei calycesque glabri in* C. cymbararifoliâ.

2. **CINERARIA** *viscosa.*

C. pedunculis unifloris, foliis pinnatifido–lobatis acutis viscidis carnulosis.

HABITAT ad Promontorium bonæ spei.

Forte varietas tantum C. humifusæ.

3. **CINERARIA** *scapiflora.*

C. pedunculis longissimis unifloris, foliis ovatis glabris duplicato-dentatis.

HABITAT ad Promontorium bonæ spei. *Masson.*

Folia duplicato-dentata vel sublobata.

4. **CINERARIA** *mitellæfolia.*

C. pedunculis subbifloris, foliis cordatis glabris laxe dentatis, petiolis simplicibus.

Senecio *cordifolius* corollis radiantibus, foliis cordatis dentatis, calycibus simplicissimis. *Linn. suppl.* 372.

HABITAT ad Promontorium bonæ spei.

5. **CINERARIA** *lanata.* Tab. 30.

C. pedunculis unifloris, foliis cordato-subrotundis septangulis subtus lanuginosis.

HABITAT in Nivariâ. *Masson.* ♄

Flores purpurei.

6. **CINERARIA** *populifolia.*

C. floribus corymbosis, foliis cordatis subangulatis subtus tomentosis, petiolis apice multijugo–appendiculatis.

Cacalia *appendiculata* fruticosa tomentosa, foliis cordatis ovatis acutis angulatis subtus tomentosis, petiolis appendiculate foliosis. *Linn. suppl.* 352.

HABITAT in insularum Canariensium *humidis. Masson.* ♄

Flores lutei. Folia Populi albæ.

7. CINERARIA *aurita.* Tab. 31.

C. floribus corymbosis, foliis cordatis subangulatis subtus tomentosis, petiolis basi biauritis.

HABITAT in Maderâ. *Masson.* ♄

Flores purpurei. Folia quoque populnea. Variat auriculis majoribus et minoribus.

8. CINERARIA *ramentosa.*

C. floribus corymbosis, foliis cordatis angulatis subtus tomentosis, petiolis superne appendiculatis, calycibus ramentosis.

Cacalia *echinata* herbacea, foliis reniformibus cordatis angulato-dentatis subtus tomentosis, foliolis calycinis tuberculatis. *Linn. suppl.* 353.

HABITAT in Canariis. *Masson.* ♄

Calyces adspersi denticulis numerosis.

9. CINERARIA *malvæfolia.* Tab. 32.

C. floribus cymosis, foliis cordatis angulatis infra subtomentosis, petiolis simplicibus..

HABITAT in Canariis *et insulâ* S. Miguel *ex* Azoribus. *Masson.* ♄

10. CINERARIA *multiflora.*

C. floribus cymosis, foliis cordato–ovatis subtus tomentosis, petiolis dimidio auritis.

HABITAT in insularum Canariensium *collibus. Masson.*

11. CINERARIA *cruenta.* Tab. 33.

C. floribus cymosis, foliis cordatis angulatis subtus purpurascentibus, petiolis basi auritis.

HABITAT in Nivariâ. *Masson.* ♄

12. CINERARIA *tussilaginis.*

C. floribus laxe paniculatis, foliis reniformi–cordatis multangulis subtus tomentosis, petiolis basi auritis.

HABITAT in Canariis, Teneriffâ. *Masson.* ☉

13. CINERARIA *lobata.* Tab. 34.

C. floribus subcorymbosis, foliis subrotundis multilobatis glabris, petiolis basi auritis, calycibus subcalyculatis.

HABITAT ad Promontorium bonæ spei. *Banks et Solander,* Masson. ♄

Bracteâ unâ alterâve sub calycibns fere calyculi instar vix distinguitur a Senecione. *Herba potius* Cinerariæ.

14. C I N E R A R I A *senecionis.*

C. floribus subcorymbosis, foliis sinuato-pinnatifidis glabris, caulinis sessilibus. *H A B I T A T ad* Promontorium bonæ spei. *Forster.* ♄

Cinerariæ *quæ calyculatæ sunt , quales* C. americana *et* lineata , *forte melius ad* Senecionem *revocandæ.*

B O L T O N I A.

C A L Y X communis subimbricatus : *squamis* linearibus. *Corolla* radiata. *Germina* compressa , verticalia. *Pappus* obsolete dentatus , bicornis. *Receptaculum* favosum.

In Astere *Calyx imbricatus. Pappus pilosus. Receptaculum nudum ex Linnæo , sed reverâ similiter alveolatum.*

In Matricariâ *Pappus nullus. Receptaculum nudum.*

In Spilantho *Corolla sæpius uniformis. Receptaculum paleaceum.*

1. B O L T O N I A *glastifolia.* Tab. 35.
B. foliis inferioribus serratis.
Matricaria glastifolia. *Hill. kew.* 19. *t.* 3.
H A B I T A T in Americâ *septentrionali.* ♃

2. B O L T O N I A *asteroides.* Tab. 36.
B. foliis integerrimis.
Matricaria *asteroides* foliis lanceolatis integris glabris obliquis. *Linn. mant.* 116.
H A B I T A T in stagnis Virginiæ. *Bartram.* ♃

B U P H T H A L M U M.

B U P H T H A L M U M *sericeum. L.* Tab. 37.
B. *sericeum* foliis oppositis approximatissimis spathulato-oblongis sericeis , calycinis squamis setaceis hirsutis , caule arboreo. *Linn. suppl.* 379.
H A B I T A T Fuertæ–venturæ *Canariensium. Masson.* ♄

S T O K E S I A.

C A L Y X communis foliaceus , subimbricatus. *Corolla* flosculosa , biformis : *in radio* corollulæ hermaphroditæ , regulares ; *in ambitu* irregulares radium

G Y N A N D R I A.

constituentes. *Filamenta* utrisque quinque. *Anthera* cylindracea. *Germen* regularibus tetragonum , irregularibus trigonum. *Stylus* filiformis. *Stigma* bipartitum , subulatum. *Pappus* filamentosus , deciduus , corollulæ æqualis , regularibus quaternus , irregularibus ternus. *Receptaculum* nudum.

Affinis Carthamo , *a quo differt Receptaculo nudo , Pappo quadrifilamentoso , floribus radiatis.*

S T O K E S I A *cyanea.* Tab. 38.

Carthamus lævis. *Hill. kew.* 57. *t. 5.*

H A B I T A T in Carolinâ *australi.* ♃

Corolla Centaureæ Cyani. *Calyx fere* Carthami.

G Y N A N D R I A.

L I M O D O R U M.

1. **L I M O D O R U M** *Tancarvilleæ.*

L. scapis radicalibus terminalibusve simplicibus , floribus pedunculatis.

L. Tancarvilleæ. *Banks. icon absque sermone.*

H A B I T A T in Chinâ. ♃

Etsi labium nectarii postice desinat in calcar brevissimum , a Limodoro *tamen separanda non videtur.*

2. **L I M O D O R U M** *tuberosum. L.*

L. scapis subsimplicibus , floribus sessilibus.

L. *tuberosum* floribus sessilibus racemosis alternis. *Linn. syst.* 594.

Helleborine americana , radice tuberosâ , foliis longis angustis , caule nudo , floribus ex rubro pallide purpurascentibus. *Mart. cent.* 50. *t.* 50. *Mill. ic. t.* 145.

H A B I T A T in Pensylvaniæ *umbrosis. Matthias Hultgren.* Marylandiâ. ♃

Racemi *simplices in omnibus speciminibus a me visis , et in Millero , sed Martynus compositos pingit.*

3. **L I M O D O R U M** *altum. L.*

L. scapis paniculatis , floribus pedunculatis.

L. *altum* floribus pedunculatis sparsis. *Linn. syst.* 594.

* *Synonymon* Plumieri excludendum , uti exhibens plantam simpliciter racemosam nec paniculatam , floribusque forte sessilibus.

H A B I T A T in Jamaicâ. *Houston.* ♃

MONOECIA.

GENESIPHYLLA.

* *Masculi flores.*

C A L Y X rotatus , sexpartitus : *laciniis* internis tribus majoribus. *Corolla* nulla. Nectarium : *Glandulæ* 6 , singula ad basin singulæ divisuræ calycis. *Filamentum* unicum , superne trifidum. *Antheræ* tres , bilobæ.

* *Feminei flores* masculis immixti apicem versus ejusdem folioli.

C A L Y X ut in mare , persistens. *Corolla* ut in mare. Nectarium : *Operculum* subtrigonum , cingens germen. *Germen* superum. *Styli* tres , tripartiti, subulati. *Stigmata* simplicia. *Capsula* trilocularis. *Semina* bina.

Si pro distincto genere stare non valeat , cum Phyllantho *potius jungenda quam cum* Xylophyllâ.

G E N E S I P H Y L L A *asplenifolia.* Tab. 39.

Xylophylla *latifolia* foliis lanceolatis , ramis teretibus. *Linn. mant.* 251.

Filicifolia hemionitidi affinis americana epiphyllanthos , folio simpliciter pinnato , radice reptatrice carnosâ , ad foliorum crenas floridâ. *Plukn. almag.* 154. *t.* 46. *f.* 7. (folium.)

Lonchitidi affinis arbor anomala , folio alato e pinnarum crenis fructifero. *Sloan. hist.* 1. 80.

Phyllanthus foliis latioribus utrinque acuminatis apicem versus crenatis. *Brown. jam.* 188. *n.* 1.

> * *Cætera* Linnæi synonyma scilicet Commelini , Pluknetii , Catesbei , Sebæ , necnon *Phyllanthus* 2 Brownei et *Phyllanthus Epiphyllanthus* L. ad *Xylophyllam falcatam* Swartzi retrahenda sunt.

H A B I T A T *in* Jamaicâ. ♄

D I O E C I A.

T A M U S.

T A M U S *elephantipes.* Tab. 40.

T. foliis reniformibus integris.

Pes Elephantis *vulgo.*

H A B I T A T *ad* Promontorium bonæ spei. *Masson.* ♃

Feminâ adhuc ignotâ certius pronuntiare inter Tamum *et* Smilacem *difficillimum. Nihilominus in mare rudimentum germinis stylo coalito calyci instructum indicat germen inferum , unde suspicari licet* Tamum *esse.*

POLYGAMIA.

MIMOSA.

1. **MIMOSA** *verticillata*. Tab. 41.

M. inermis, foliis verticillatis linearibus pungentibus.

HABITAT in Terrâ Van–Diemen *Novæ-Hollandiæ. Nelson.* ♄

In plantâ nascente folia duo vel tria primordialia bipinnata.

2. **MIMOSA** *Houstoni.*

M. inermis foliis bipinnatis abruptis subsexjugis, pinnulis multijugis, foliolis subconfluentibus, racemo composito terminali.

Gleditschia *inermis* caule inermi. *Linn. spec.* 1509.

Acacia americana non spinosa, flore purpureo, staminibus longissimis, siliquis planis villosis, pinnis foliorum tenuissimis. *Houst. mss. p.* 22. *Mill. icon.* 4. *t.* 5.

Mimosa. *Houst. rel.* 12. *t.* 26.

HABITAT in Verâ-Cruce. *Houston.* ♄

Folia *subtus pilosa.* Inflorescentia *ut in* M. grandiflorâ, *sed* Flores *minores.* Corollæ *villosæ, persistentes.* Legumina *parallelogramma, acuminata, plana, seminibus elevata, admodum tomentosa, rufa.* Semina *oblonga, compressa, utrinque zonâ notata, marginibus suturæ utrisque alterius inserta.*

Hæc est Gleditschia inermis *Linnæi. Recentiores autores quales* Duhamel, Du Roi, *et alii, varietatem inermem* Gleditschiæ triacanthos *pro* Gleditschiâ inermi *habuere.*

3. **MIMOSA** *grandiflora.* Tab. 42.

M. inermis, foliis abrupte bipinnatis multijugis, pinnulis multijugis, foliolis distinctissimis, racemo composito terminali.

Acacia non spinosa indiæ orientalis, foliis perexeguis, virgulis lanugine ferrugineâ villosis. *Plukn. amalth.* 3.

HABITAT in Indiâ *orientali.* ♄

Affinis quam plurimum M. Houstoni, *a quâ differt pinnulis crebrioribus, foliolisque distinctissimis basi ovatis, dum in* M. Houstoni *juxta rachidem confluentibus basi truncatis foliumque pinnatifidum mentientibus.*

CRYPTOGAMIA.

DICKSONIA.

FRUCTIFICATIONES subrotundæ, margini averso frondis subjectæ.

CRYPTOGAMIA.

CALYX *communis* reniformis , unilocularis , florifer clausus , longitudinaliter fructifer dehiscens. *Valvula exterior* ex ipsâ substantiâ folii ; *interior* membranacea. *Flosculi* ignoti. *Capsulæ* numerosæ, pedicellatæ, *Receptaculo* longitudinali affixæ. *Semina* numerosissima , minuta.

1. DICKSONIA *arborescens.* Tab. 43.

D. frondibus supradecompositis villosis , foliolis subintegris , caule arboreo.

HABITAT *in insulâ* Sanctâ Helenâ. *Banks et Solander.* ♄

2. DICKSONIA *Culcita.*

D. frondibus supradecompositis glabris, foliolis serratis.

Polydopium ? *Baromets* frondibus bipinnatis , pinnis pinnatifidis lanceolatis serratis , radicibus lanatis. *Linn. spec.* 1553 ?

Agnus scythicus aut vegetabilis Boramets dictus autoribus fabulosis ? *Scal. subt. exerc.* 181. §. 29. *Port. phyt. l.* 4. *c.* 4. *Duret. hist.* 331. *Licet. spont. l.* 3. *c.* 45.

The Tartarian Lamb. *Sloan. act. angl.* 1698. *n.* 247. *pag.* 461. *tab.* 247. *f.* 5 ? (radix obversa.)

Agnus scythicus vegetabilis Borametz dictus. *Breyn. act. angl.* 1725. *n.* 390. *v.* 353. *t.* 390 ? (radix obversa.)

> * *Consul.* de Agno scythico *Deusing. diss.* 598. *Breyn. loc. cit.* et *Kœmpf. amœn.* 505. Si *Baromets* et *D. Culcita* non sint eadem planta , quod, etsi patriæ tam remotæ, vix incertum , procul dubio Agnus scythicus alia erit Filicis species.

Feila Brom *Maderensibus vulgo.*

HABITAT *in insulâ* S. Miguel *ex* Azoribus. *Masson.* ♃

E radicibus Culcitas conficiunt incolæ.

Addenda et emendanda.

POLYGAMIA.

EUCLEA.

CALYX quinquedentatus, parvulus, persistens. *Corolla* monopetala, quinquepartita, calyce major , receptaculo inserta : *laciniis* ovatis , obtusis , patentibus. *Filamenta* circiter 15 , brevia , receptaculo inserta. *Antheræ* erectæ , biloculares , tetragonæ, villosiusculæ, corollâ breviores. *Germen* superum, pyramidato-ovatum. *Styli* duo , longitud. staminum. *Stigmata* simplicia. *Capsula* baccata, i. e. pulpâ induta , subrotunda , tricornis , trilocularis , trivalvis. *Semina* solitaria , subrotunda , arillata , uno alterove abortiente.

POLYGAMIA.

Dantur flores hermaphroditi, et hermaphroditi masculi sc. germine abortivo, unde videretur polygama. Planta femina, si exstat, me fugit.

EUCLEA *racemosa. L.*

E. racemosa. *Linn.* (*Murr.*) *syst.* 747. *ed.* 13^a. *Linn. suppl.* 67. 428. *Thunb. gen.* 5. *pag.* 85.

Celastrus *corniculatus* foliis ovalibus integerrimis perennantibus, capsulâ tricorni. *pag.* 6.

Evonymus africanus, foliis laurinis, fructu aculeato. *Breyn. icon. t.* 22. *f.* 3.

Padus foliis subrotundis, fructu racemoso. *Burm. afr.* 238. *t.* 84. *f.* 1. (Autor hîc fructum infantem forte exhibet.)

Evonymus foliis subrotundis integris, fructu corniculato. *Burm. afr.* 260. *t.* 97. *f.* 1.

HABITAT ad Promontorium bonæ spei. *Masson.* ♄

Capsulæ absolute Celastri *nisi baccatæ et cornutæ, unde, flore mihi ignoto, pro* Celastro corniculato *in hoc opere habueram. Specimina fructifera hujus* Celastri corniculati *tam similia* E. racemosæ *quam ovum ovo. Miror nihilominus, vixque crederes plantam digynam, ut* Eucleam, *gaudere fructu triloculari. Nec cum stylis duobus multo melius quadrat bacca monosperma quam huic generi assignat Thunbergius. Linnæus baccam dicit bilocularem. Ulterius ergo de fructu ab autoptis inquirendum.*

WITHERINGIA.

(TETRANDRIA monogynia.)

CARACTER ESSENTIALIS.

CALYX quadridentatus. *Corolla* campanulata. *Nectarium* polymorphum , quadrilobum , corollæ adnatum. *Filamenta* corollæ adnata. *Antheræ* lateribus dehiscentes. *Germen* superum. *Bacca* polysperma.

In memoriam celeberr. Gulielmi WITHERING , *Doct. Med. Soc. reg. Lond. Soc. autoris operis inscripti :* Botanical arrangement of British plants.

WITHERINGIA solanacea.

HABITAT *in* Americâ *meridionali.* ♃

PLANTA habitu Physalidis , aut Solani.

* *Descensus.*

RADIX fasciculata , fusiformis , carnosa , nunc subsimplex , nunc ramosa , descendens, magna , cinerea.

* *Ascensus.*

CAULES plurimi e radice , erecti , apice dichotomi , teretes lineis tribus e petiolis ultimis decurrentibus , villosi , obscure purpurascentes , semipedales s. vix pedales.

RAMI tantum ad apicem ; breves , patuli , caulibus conformes.

* *Frondescentia.*

FOLIA alterna , superne ubi planta inflorescere cœpit bina , petiolata , subacuminata , cordata , integra , subundulata , nervosa , rugosa : nervis subtus prominentibus , supra prominulis ; costâ ad paginam pronam vix purpurascente ; villosa , patentia , 3 poll. long. 2 poll. lat.

PETIOLI subtus teretes , supra plani uninerves , villosi , obscure purpurei , folio sexies breviores.

* *Inflorescentia.*

FLORES axillares , confertissimi , cernui , lutei , 6 lin. lat.

PEDUNCULI reflexi , apice incrassati , quasi clavati , petiolis longiores.

EXPLICATIO TABULÆ.

PLANTA proportione naturali.

1. *Flos* antice ,		5. *Stamen* ,	
2. —— postice ,	} pr. nat.	6. *Pistillum* ,	} prop. nat.
3. *Corolla* postice ,			
4. ——— secta ostendens *Stamina* et *Nectarium*,			

* *Fructificatio.*

CALYX. *Perianthium* inferum , monophyllum , obsolete modiceque quadridentatum , brevissimum , nudiusculum , persistens.

COROLLA monopetala , subcampanulata , quadripartita , receptaculo inserta , calyce longe major. *Tubus* brevis , subrotundus , vix tetragonus. *Laciniæ* lanceolatæ , acutæ , patentes , subrevolutæ.

NECTARIUM constans 1 . *Operculo* brevissimo subvilloso corollam infra divisuras cingente. 2°. *Appendiculâ* parvulâ subrotundâ corollæ adnatâ utrinque ad basin singuli filamenti. 3°. *Foveolis* 4 , extrorsum vix manifestis , magnâ copiâ mellis impletis , quarum limites sunt , superne operculum corollæ , inferne appendix filamentorum , lateraliter ipsa filamenta.

STAMINA. *Filamenta* 4 , erecta , teretiuscula , clavata , villosa , brevia , dimidiæ corollæ adnata. *Antheræ* ovatæ , biloculares , vix peltatæ , lateribus dehiscentes , luteolæ , conniventes.

PISTILLUM. *Germen* superum , ovatum. *Stylus* filiformis , staminibus vix longior. *Stigma* capitatum , viride.

PERICARPIUM (quale deprehenditur ex floribus). *Bacca* bilocularis ? intra quam *Receptaculum* ejusdem formæ , bipartitum.

SEMINA numerosa , receptaculo inserta.

Patria assignatur America meridionalis. Primum floruit apud *Rob. Jac.* PETRE , *Parem Anglum.* Hodie viget in Horto Kewensi. Quotannis floret æstate , sed nondum fructus tulit. Hucusque avulsis a matre viviradicibus propagari videtur. In tepidario excolitur.

DIAGNOSTICON.

WITHERINGIA differt a *Solano* partium numero , antheris imperforatis , nectario : ab *Atropâ* numero quaternario , nectario : ab *Aquartiâ* calyce æquali nec laciniis alternis duplo vel triplo majoribus , limbo corollæ lanceolato nec lineari longissimo , antheris latere dehiscentibus nec apice perforatis , denique nectario.

CHLORANTHUS.

NIGRINA. *Thunb. gen.*

(TETRANDRIA monogynia.)

CARACTER ESSENTIALIS.

PERIANTHIUM duplex. *Exterius* bracteæforme s. mera Bractea. *Proprium:* Squamula semisupera, lateri germinis exteriori adnata. *Petalum* semisuperum, dimidiatum, trifidum, lateri germinis insidens, -perianthii proprii axillare, antheriferum. *Antheræ* petalo adnatæ. *Germen* semiinferum, petaligerum. *Stylus* nullus. *Stigma* capitatum. *Bacca* monosperma.

A vocibus græcis ΧΛΩΡΟΣ *viridis, et* Ἄνθος flos, *dixit Olaus* SWARTZ *, quia flores gaudent colore herbaceo.*

CHLORANTHUS inconspicuus.

C. inconspicuus. *Swartz. act. lond.* 1787. *p.* 359. *t.* 14.
Nigrina spicata. *Thunb. gen.* 3. 59. *jap.* 65.
Tchin-Tchu-lan-hoa s. Tchu-lan *Sinensibus vulgo.*

HABITAT in Chinâ. ♄

SUFFRUTEX perennans, glaber, stolonifer, habitu *Theæ.*

* *Descensus.*
RADIX *Rusci*, ramosa, alba, stolonifera.

* *Ascensus.*
CAULES e radice plurimi, basi procumbentes, dein suberecti, parce ramosi, teretes, nodosi, grisei. *Nodi* prope terram radicantes : alterni et intermedii nonnunquam aphylli, sed stipulis annulati ut cæteri.

RAMI oppositi, patuli, teretes, virides, nodosi, subarticulati : geniculis annulatis.

* *Frondescentia.*
FOLIA opposita, oblongo-ovata, acuta, crenato-serrata : serraturis apice morbificatis ; margine revoluta, subrugosa : venis distantibus subtus tantum prominentibus ; viridia,

EXPLICATIO TABULÆ.

PLANTA proportione naturali.

1. Sectio *Spicæ*, alterâ icone auctâ.
2. *Flos* introrsum,
3. —— extrorsum,   } aucta.
4. *Petalum* introrsum,
5. —— extrorsum,

6. *Germen* antice,   } auctum.
7. —— lateraliter,
8. *Bacca* lateraliter, prop. nat.
9. —— antice aucta.
10. *Semen* prop. nat

concolora, glaberrima, patentia, plana, persistentia, 2-3 poll. long. 18-20 lin. lat.

PETIOLI folio quater breviores, teretes, supra unisulci, basi desinentes in annulum amplexicaulem, adnectentem

STIPULAS utrinque duas, subulatas, erectas, persistentes.

* *Inflorescentia.*

PANICULÆ terminales, erectæ, laxæ, bracteatæ, compositæ *Spicis* decussatis patulis, 1 ½ poll. long.

FLORES sessiles, oppositi, decussati, herbacei s. luteoli, 1 lin. long.

BRACTEÆ sessiles, lanceolatæ, acutæ, concavæ, adpressæ, persistentes, sub spicis.

* *Fructificatio.*

CALYX. *Perianthium* duplex, persistens.

IMPROPRIUM (*quod melius Bracteam dicas*) *inferius* monophyllum, squamiforme, lanceolatum, acutum, patulum, bracteis cæteris conforme, breve, ½ lin. long.

PROPRIUM *superius. Squamula* semisupera, lateri germinis exteriori adnata, acuta, subovata, concava, brevissima.

COROLLA. *Petalum* semisuperum, laterale, perianthii proprii axillare, clivo germinis exteriori, instar receptaculi germini adnati, inter germen et perianthium proprium medii, impositum, subrotundum, dimidiatum, trifidum, trigonum, incurvum, concavum, extus convexum, crassum, concamerationis instar genitalia abscondens, antheriferum, deciduum : *laciniis* acutis; incurvis; intermediâ duplo productiore.

STAMINA. *Filamenta* nulla. *Antheræ* 4, oblongiusculæ, bivalves, lateri exteriori singulæ laciniæ corollinæ introrsum adnatæ, herbaceæ.

PISTILLUM. *Germen* respectu perianthii proprii et corollæ superum simul et inferum, obsolete ovatum. *Stylus* nullus, seu vix ullus. *Stigma* capitatum, subbivalve, nonnunquam bilobum.

PERICARPIUM. *Bacca* ovalis, stylo acuminata, nunc ad apicem nec ad latus ut in germine notata cicatrice receptaculi et petali basi pellucida, unilocularis.

> * *Perianthium* proprium cicatrixque petali lapsi accrescente fructu sensim elevantur, donec apici baccæ insideant ; unde colligendum Germen revera inferum esse, etsi potius superum appareat.

SEMEN unicum, subrotundum.

Viva allata fuit e Chinâ in Angliam a *Jac. LIND, D. M.* anno 1781. Floruit dum navis ATLAS adveheret. Florentem delineandam curavi in Horto *Jac. LEE,* moxque fructiferam in Horto regio Kewensi observavi. Sæpissime eodem anno floret, fructusque nonnullos perficit. Excolitur in caldario, surculisque et stolonibus regeneratur.

Sinensibus misceri foliis *Theæ*, *Theam*que suavius olere *Doctor Lind* narrabat, sed *Chloranthus* omnino inodorus est. In quem usum excolatur a Sinensibus planta minime speciosa quam in pluribus plantarum hortensium in Chinâ depictarum collectaneis vidi, adhuc latet.

WITHERINGIA solanacea.

P. J. Redouté del.

Malevre sculp.

CHLORANTHUS inconspicuus.

Jac. Sowerby del.

Juillet sculp.

CAMPANULA Prismatocarpus.

4.

Jac. Sowerby del.

Juillet sculp.

LIGHTFOOTIA oxycoccoides.

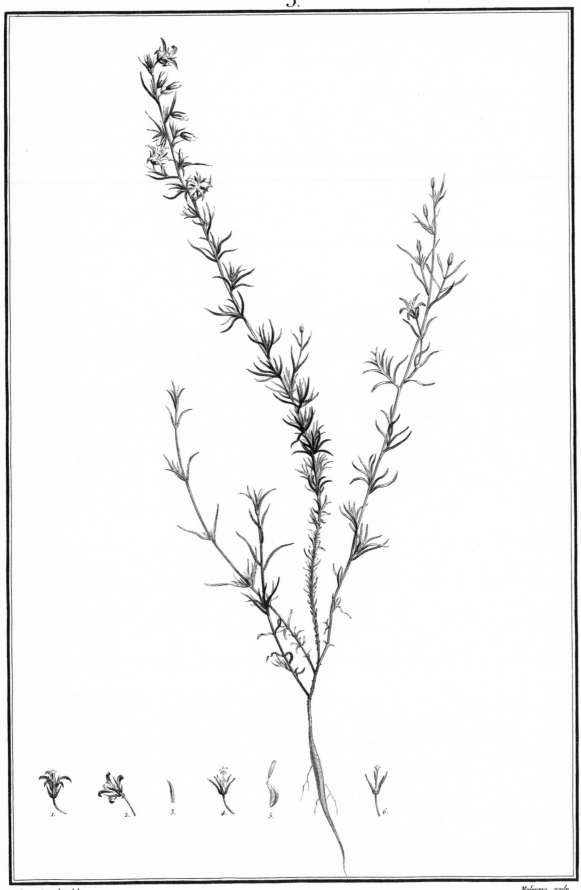

LIGHTFOOTIA subulata.

Jac. Sowerby del.

Juillet sculp.

RoËLLA decurrens.

Jac. Sowerby del.

Juillet sculp.

HAMELIA grandiflora.

8.

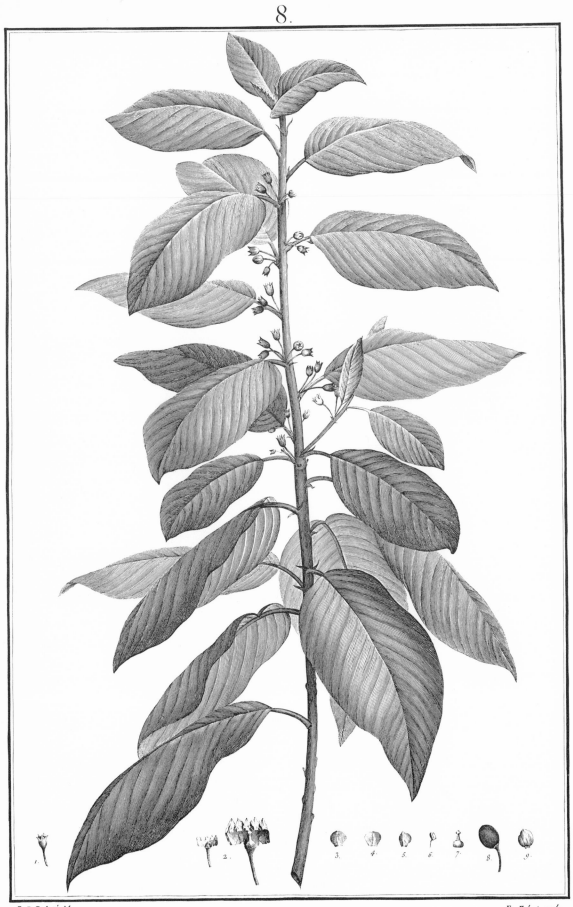

P. J. Redouté del.

Fr. Hubert sculp.

RHAMNUS latifolius.

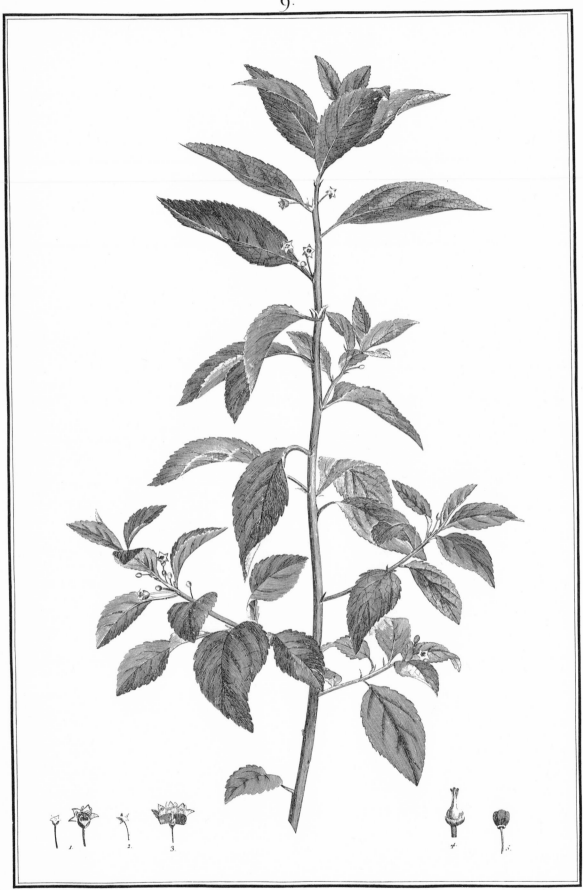

Jac. Sowerby del.

Juillet sculp.

R H A M N U S prinoides.

P. J. Redouté del.

Fr. Hubert sculp.

CELASTRUS caſsinoides.

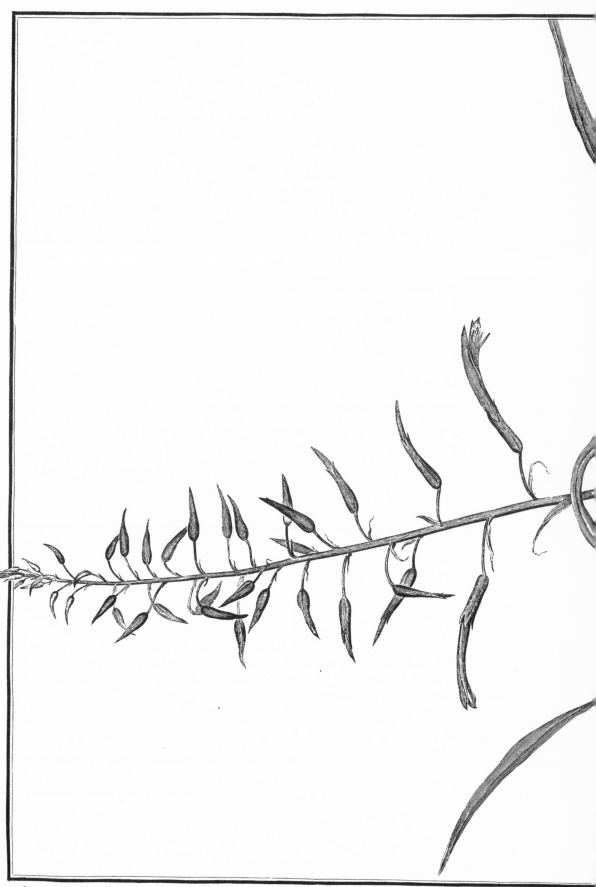

PITCAIRN

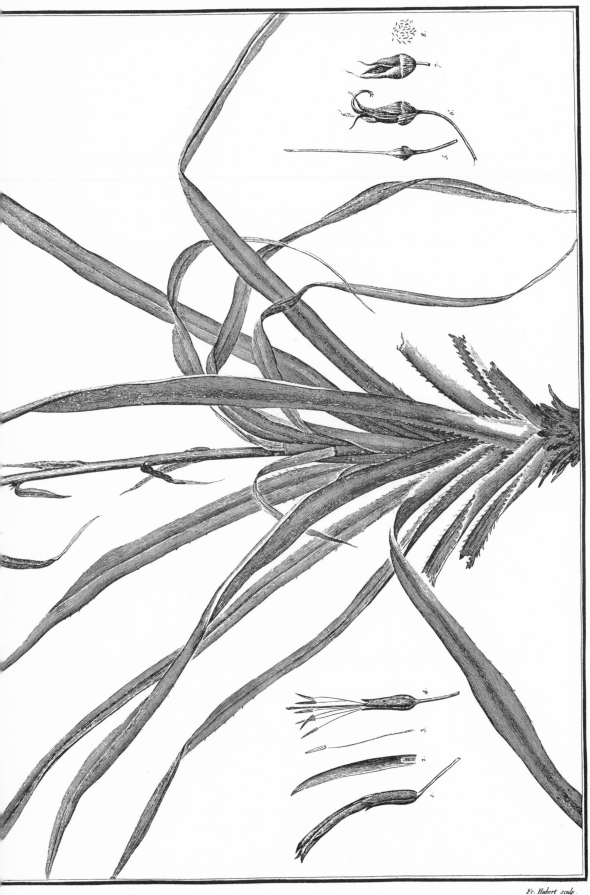

A bromeliæfolia.

Fr. Hubert sculp.

TRADESC

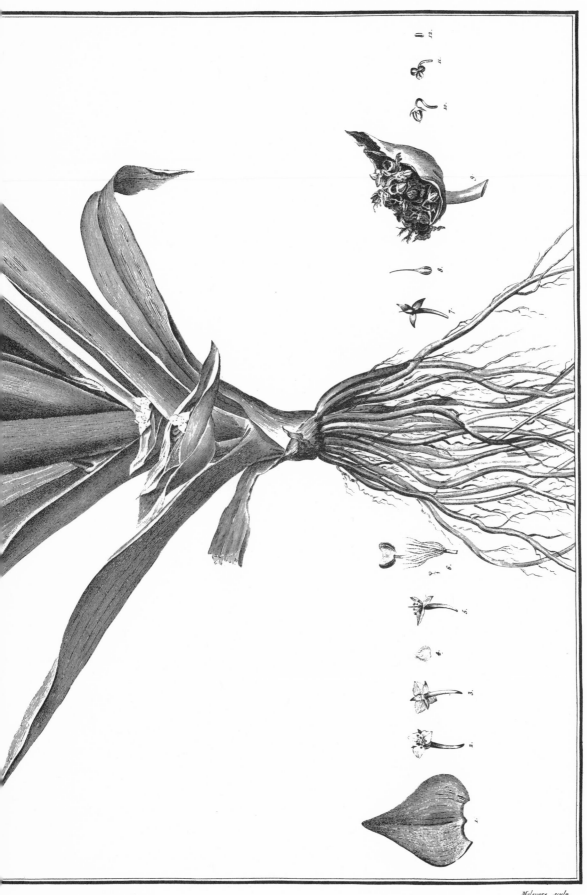

T I A difcolor.

J. G. Bruguiere del.

Maleuvre sculp.

A M A R Y L L I S ſpiralis.

Pernotin del.

AMARYL

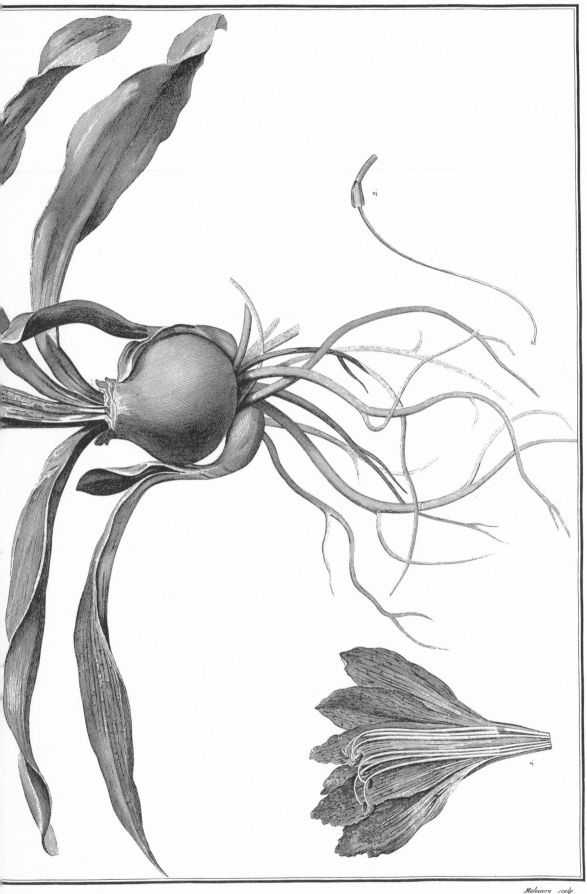

s   reticulata.

Maleuvre sculp.

P. J. Redouté del.

A M A R Y L

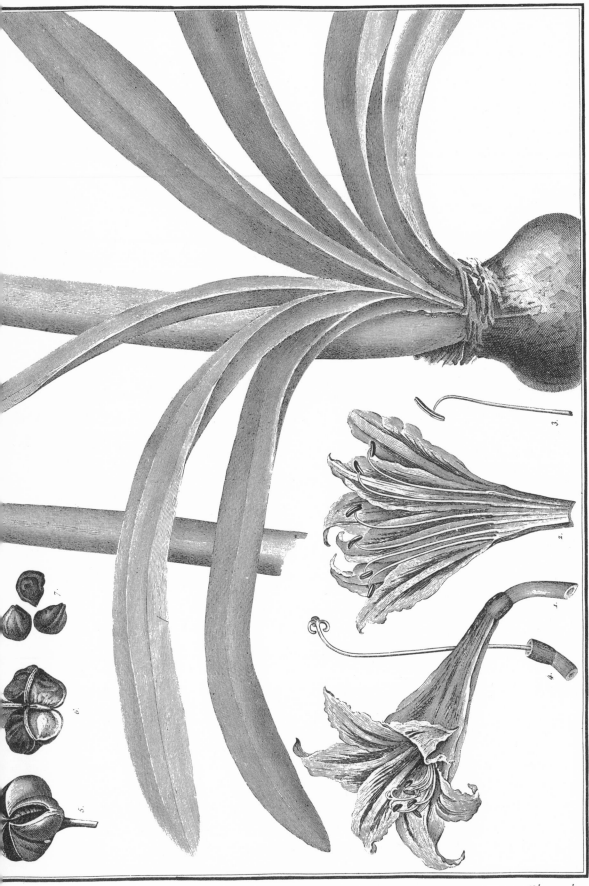

I S vittata.

Malewre sculp.

AMARY

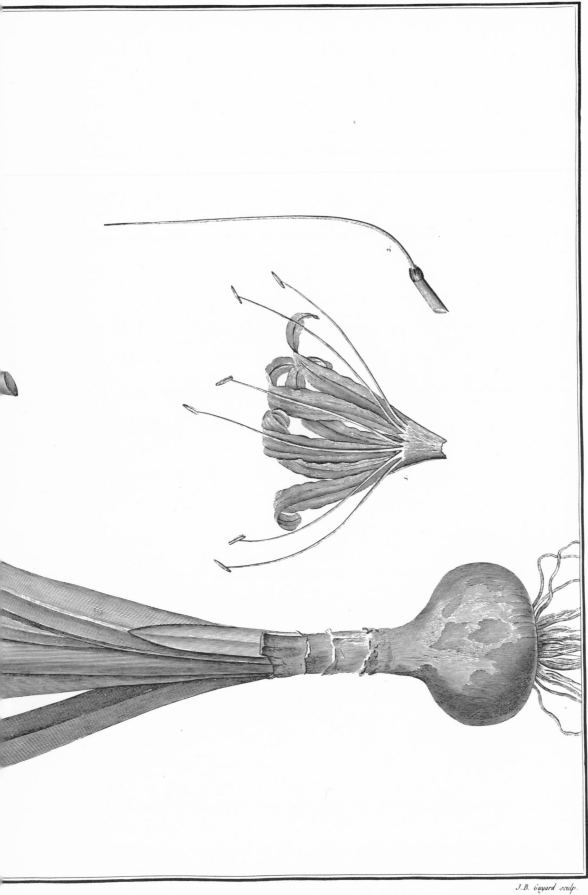

I S   aurea.

Amaryl

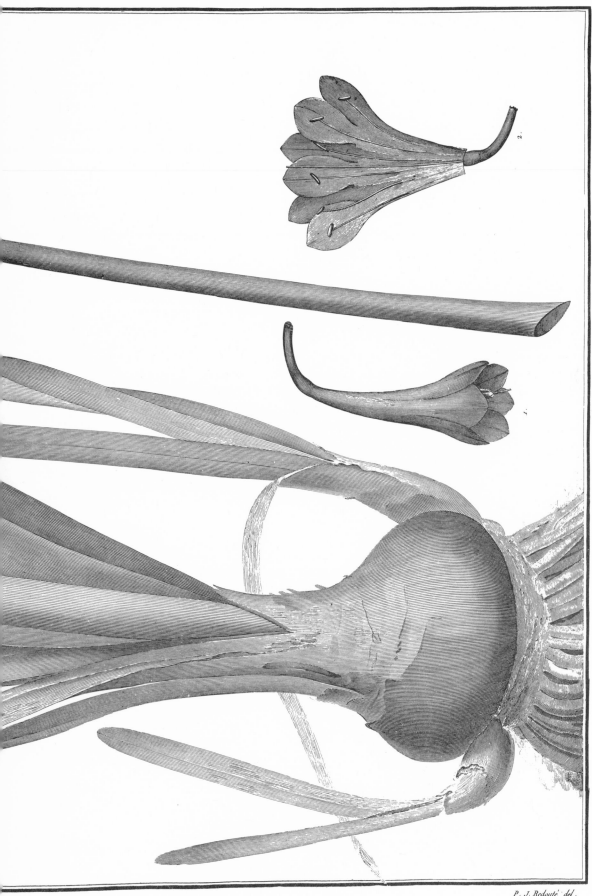

S   Umbella.

AMARYLLIS cinnamomea.

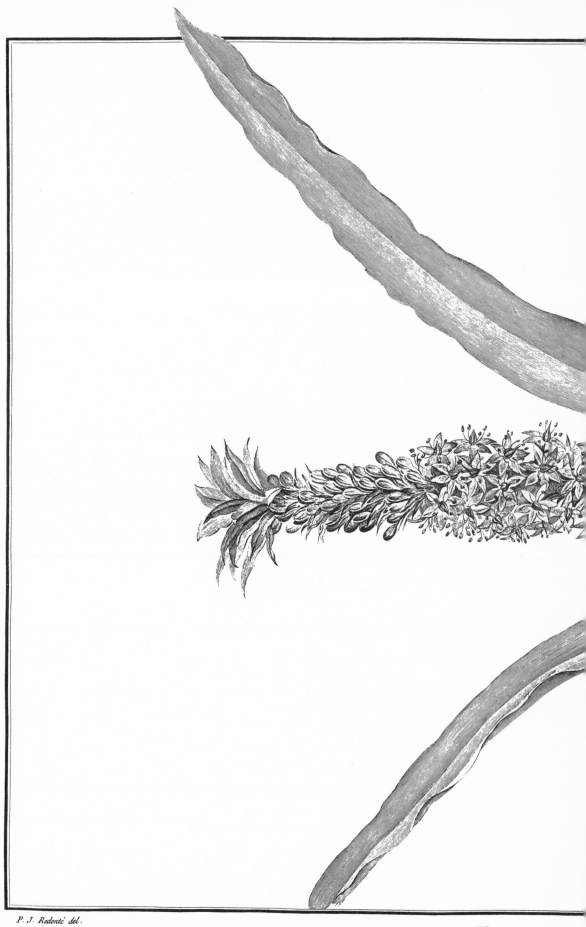

Eucom

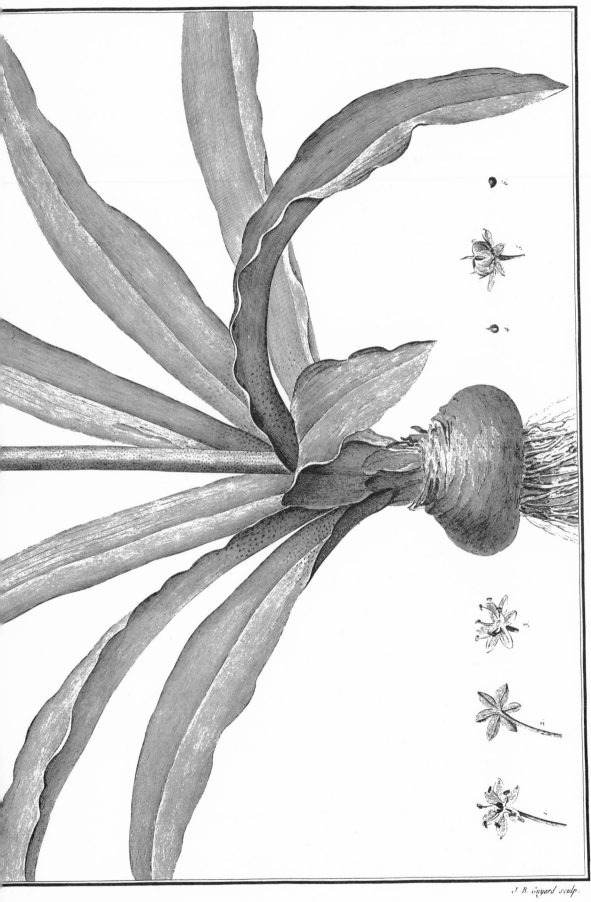

punctata.

J. B. Guyard sculp.

KOËLREUT

Steph. Voysard sculp.

R I A   paniculata.

L. J. Redouté del.

Fr. Hubert sculp.

EUCALYPTUS obliqua.

P. J. Redouté del.

Fr. Hubert sculp.

L A V A N D U L A viridis.

Jac. Sowerby del.

Juillet sculp

BYSTROPOGON plumofum.

P. J. Redouté del.

Fr. Hubert sculp.

B Y S T R O P O G O N punctatum.

DIGITALIS Sceptrum. L.

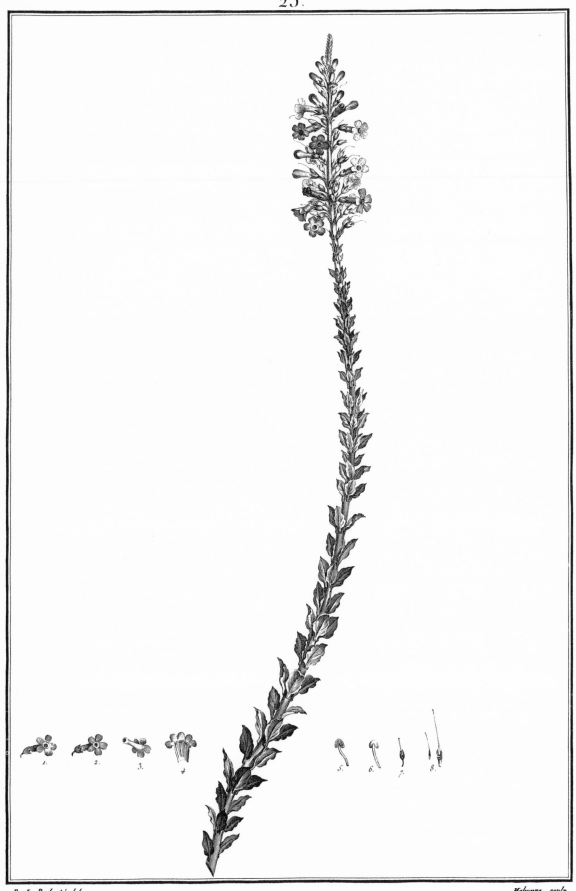

CAPRARIA undulata.

Jac. Sowerby pinx.

Malœuvre sculp.

ASPALATHUS pedunculata.

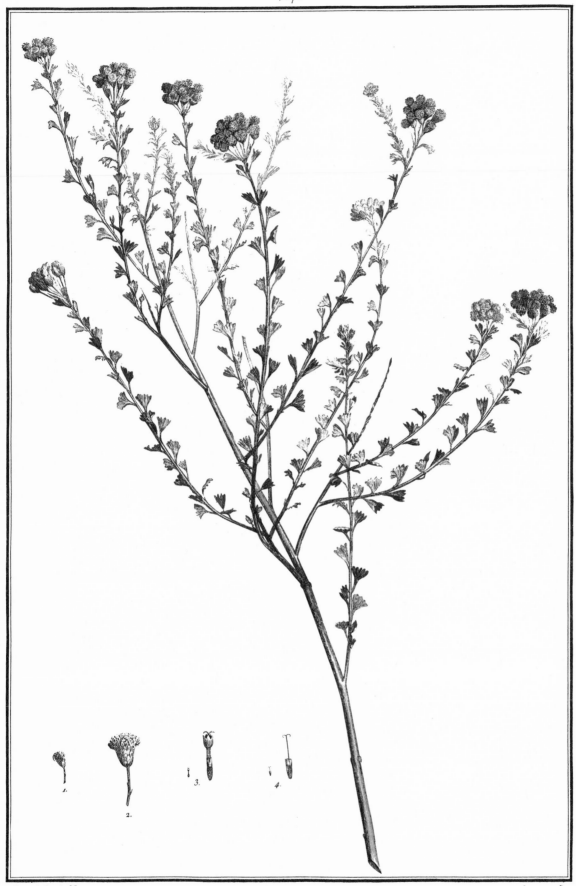

T A N A C E T U M flabelliforme.

P. J. Redouté del.

J. B. Gayard sculp.

ARTEMISIA argentea.

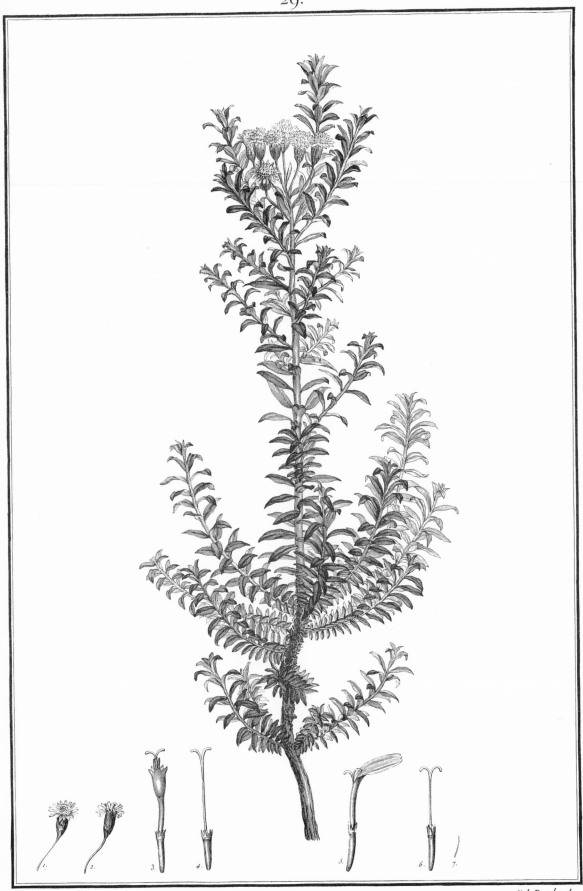

Jac. Sowerby del.

Steph. Voysard sculp.

RELHANIA squarrofa.

P. J. Redouté del.

J. B. Guyard sculp.

CINERARIA lanata.

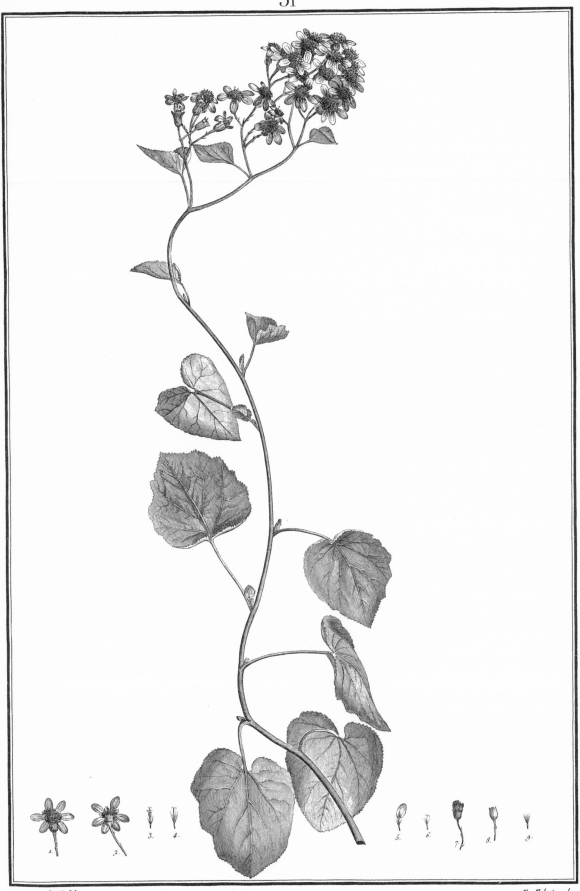

P. J. Redouté del.

Fr. Hubert sculp.

CINERARIA aurita

P. J. Redouté del.

Fr. Hubert sculp.

CINERARIA malvæfolia

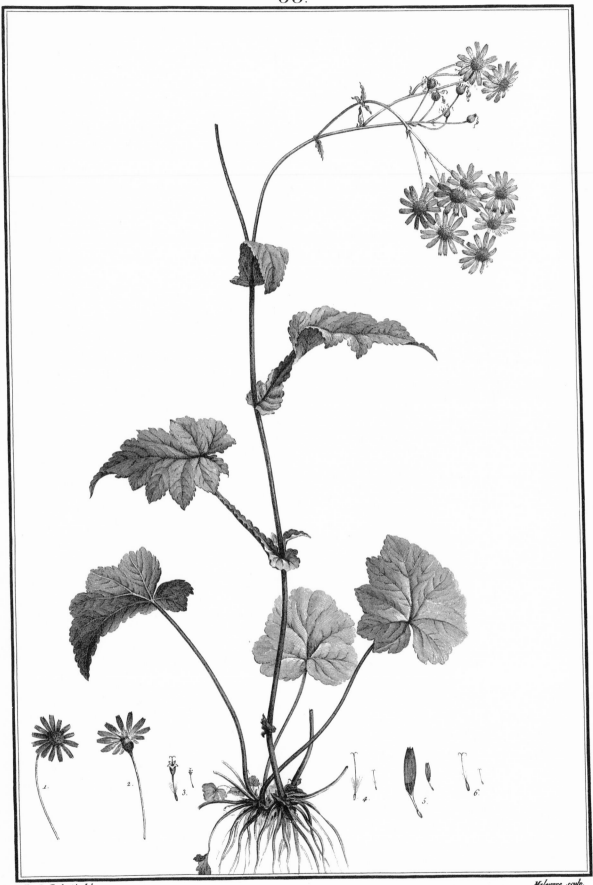

P. J. Redouté del.

Malœvre sculp.

CINERARIA cruenta.

P. J. Redouté del.

Fr. Hubert sculp.

CINERARIA lobata.

Index to Latin names of plants

General index

COLOPHON

THE TYPE OF THE NEW TEXT IS THE SPECTRUM MONOTYPE.
THE ORIGINAL OF THIS TYPE WAS DESIGNED BY JAN VAN KRIMPEN IN 1943
FOR JOH. ENSCHEDÉ EN ZONEN, HAARLEM. THE COMPOSITION,
THE LITHOGRAPHY OF THE PLATES AND THE PRINTING IN OFFSET ARE BY
JOH. ENSCHEDÉ EN ZONEN. THE PAPER IS SUPERIOR WOODFREE OFFSET PAPER.
THE BINDING IS BY J. BRANDT & ZN, AMSTERDAM.

THIS EDITION IS LIMITED TO 2,000 COPIES.